Music, Memory, and Meaning

Music, Memory, and Meaning

How to Effectively Use Music to Connect with Aging Loved Ones

MEREDITH HAMONS, TARA JENKINS, AND CATHY BEFI-HENSEL

If any copyrighted materials have inadvertently been used
in this work without proper credit or permissions, please
contact the publisher.

Music, Memory, and Meaning
© 2017 Hamons, Jenkins, & Befi-Hensel
Published by:
Whelk and Waters Publishing

Book design by TLC Graphics, www.TLCGraphics.com
Cover: Tamara Dever; Interior: Marisa Jackson

Printed in the U.S.A.

ISBN-13: 978-0-9992469-0-0

Table of Contents

Introduction

As music therapists, all three of us are passionate about working with older adults through music and are excited to witness on a daily basis the powerful positive effect music can have with aging loved ones. We firmly believe music can touch us in ways that go beyond words and also know that music affects the brain and neurological processes across more areas than any other sensory stimuli. Music stimulates deep emotions, it motivates and inspires us, and helps us hold onto memories and our identity. Most importantly in our work, music helps us transcend impairments, decline, and disease. While aging brings wisdom, it can unfortunately bring with it physical, cognitive, and emotional challenges, which is when the power of music becomes so essential.

Although the use of music in medicine has been documented as far back as ancient Egypt and Biblical times, music therapy only emerged as a formalized profession in the 1940s. Currently there are around 7,000 board-certified music therapists in the United States. The three of us love what we do and are happy to see increased awareness about the power of music in general as well as the current "buzz" about the success of music specifically with older adults. While we would love to see every senior care community have access to music therapy services, in a broader sense we want to see music used more often and more effectively in the daily care of older adults. Together, the three of us have 30 years of experience working with the senior population. We are passionate about advocating for both individuals living with the challenges of aging, as well as those who take on the responsibility of caring for them.

Our goal was to create a resource that anyone working with older adults can use, regardless of musical ability or experience. "Older Adult" (or "loved one," which is how we will refer to them throughout this book) can be a complicated term as everyone ages differently. This book is primarily designed for use with any older adult living with cognitive decline and memory loss, regardless of whether he or she has a dementia diagnosis and regardless of how mild or severe those challenges may be. Throughout this book, we will be referring to the individual caring for a loved one as "caregiver." The relationship between loved one and caregiver can present itself in a variety of ways and we want to honor and respect each of those relationships.

While this book will highlight why music is so effective with older adults and provide general strategies on how best to use music, it is intended primarily as a practical resource that can be put to use immediately. It includes extensive playlist examples and over 100 engaged listening discussions for you to share with your loved one. Designed to be easy to use, this book requires no additional resources beyond a device to play music. We hope this resource will help foster a closer connection with your aging loved one and provide meaning, comfort, and purpose to his or her daily life.

— Meredith, Tara, and Cathy

Part One

Introduction to Using Music with Older Adults

THE POWER AND POTENTIAL OF MUSIC

The power and potential of music is increasingly the subject of more research, attention, and media coverage. The purpose of this book is to explore how to apply this information in ways that are meaningful and practical with older adults living with cognitive decline and/or dementia. Everyone can reap the benefits that come from enjoying music, and this book is written to help aging loved ones and their caregivers make the most of the music listening experience. When sharing music with your loved one, it is also important to recognize both your limitations and the scope of this book. This book is designed to help you and your loved one effectively enjoy music together; it is not a guide to using music as therapy.

The field of music therapy is dedicated to using music specifically to improve functioning in such areas as cognition, communication, motor skills, social skills, and mental and emotional health. While treatment approaches vary and music therapists work with a wide variety of ages, populations, and diagnoses, those practicing music therapy are trained to achieve greater response levels and measurable gains on non-musical goals than those using music recreationally. Music therapists earn the credential MT-BC (music therapist, board certified) after completing a Bachelor's degree program, a clinical internship, and passing the Board Certification Examination. While music therapists are formally trained to harness the therapeutic benefits of music, there are still many non-clinical ways to use music to support aging loved ones, which is the focus of this book.

Even in a recreational setting, caregivers should be aware that sometimes older adults living with cognitive decline and/or dementia can become aggressive, tearful, or even violent. If, while listening to music, your loved one experiences an emotional state that you do not feel comfortable handling, please seek assistance from a music therapist, psychologist, medical doctor, or another healthcare professional as appropriate. For further suggestions on how to proceed in such situations, see "Additional Considerations and Resources" on page 13.

Articles, books, and even commercials often reference the "power" of music. But what is it about music that makes it so powerful? Why does music have such a strong impact on every individual and how can that effect be used for healing purposes? Music is one of the very first things a person responds to at the beginning of life and one of the very last things a person can still respond to at the end. It's not hard to imagine the emotional impact or therapeutic potential of a medium that literally affects everyone from even before birth until death. Furthermore, music has been a part of human cultures for all of recorded history. In fact, music was an integral part of healing rituals in many ancient civilizations. Music is loved almost universally. It's enjoyable, it's motivational, and it's a deeply ingrained part of culture and the human experience. Individuals do not need to be told *to* respond to music or taught *how* to respond to music, their bodies and brains do it naturally, because musical processing is an innate part of human biology and neurology. As more and more research is being completed, music is being viewed not only as an enjoyable pastime or an integral part of human history, but also something that elicits a response on the biological level. Dale Taylor, PhD, MT-BC (1997) writes, "Music influences human behavior by affecting the brain and subsequently other bodily structures in ways that are observable, identifiable, measurable, and predictable, thereby providing the necessary foundation for its use in treatment procedures." Music can alter brain chemistry and can affect heart rate, breath rate, and blood pressure in addition to changing both brain structure and the way neurons fire. In fact, more and more studies in the past three decades have been focused on music and the brain. Researchers are finding that music is the only sensory input that is processed in the entire brain simultaneously. Neuroscientists are even studying musical processing in the brain in order to gain a better understanding of how the brain functions. Music is unique in the way it is processed throughout the entire brain and can be used to change and strengthen specific neural networks.

It's natural to think about music emotionally first. The emotional draw of music is *so* essential because it is an innate response that appears throughout one's entire life. Emotional responses to music are observable from very young infants all the way to older adults living with advanced dementia. Older adults often have strong emotional responses to music even when they are no longer verbally communicating or otherwise responding to typical methods of care. Providing older adults with cognitive decline and/or dementia a way to access, experience, and express a range of emotions is a substantial improvement to their quality of life. As memories fade, so does their sense of self. For those who are losing their ability to interact with others and the world around them in a meaningful way, and struggling to maintain their identity and personality, connecting to music emotionally allows them to connect with others as well as to their own past experiences.

In addition to the emotional component of music, rhythm plays a huge role in one's ability to connect with music. It is a crucial aspect of music's effectiveness when working with aging older adults. While it may be easy for individuals to dismiss their rhythmic abilities and it's common to hear statements such as "I don't have a good sense of rhythm" or "I'm just not musical," keep in mind the human body is naturally rhythmic. A beating heart, breathing, walking, etc. all have rhythm and, even with no musical training, the body responds automatically to the rhythm in music. Every individual at one point or another has tapped, clapped, or moved along with a piece of music without thinking about it. Anyone observing even the smallest of children has seen their natural inclination to move and dance with music. Studies show that even individuals with advanced dementia will often still respond to rhythmic musical interventions, even long after their ability to speak has been lost. Just like rhythm is the first thing a developing infant can respond to musically, it is often the last thing an individual with late-stage dementia can respond to as well. Once again, the key to music's effectiveness is that it is processed at an instinctive biological level. Engagement comes naturally and lasts a lifetime.

In addition to the innate response to music and rhythm, music is so powerful because of how much it accompanies life both personally and culturally. Music is present throughout daily life in so many ways, whether it's learning the ABCs, singing "Happy Birthday" at a celebration with loved ones, dancing at a wedding, or singing hymns at a funeral. Culturally, music is an integral part of the most joyous celebrations and ceremonies as well as the saddest and most challenging occasions. Take a moment and think about what music you enjoy and why. What memories and feelings come to mind? Are you transported somewhere special when you hear it? Does it remind you of a particular person? Does it bring about feelings of joy? Sadness? Excitement? Everyone has particular songs that they connect with on an emotional level. Additionally, music that is part of shared experiences connects people to each other through shared memories and shared emotional responses. Henry Wadsworth Longfellow once said, "Music is the universal language of mankind." Music connects humans to the deepest part of themselves and to one another.

Given how deeply music is ingrained biologically, neurologically, culturally, and personally, it is easy to see why music can be so powerful regardless of age or ability. This becomes crucial for older adults living with cognitive decline and/or dementia. Dementia, cognitive decline, and memory loss can come with different symptoms for different people, and can bring with it feelings of fear, anger, grief, and loss in both the person diagnosed and those who care for him or her. Anyone personally affected by this disease knows that their loved one is so much more than this diagnosis. It is important that they continue to be defined by their abil-

ities, and not seen only for their limitations. Both live and recorded music can help assist in creating meaningful connections. Music encourages people to see each other for who they are regardless of limitations or disease. It can be a valuable tool to help foster meaningful visits and interactions, in addition to providing your loved one with care and support.

Musical processing is generalized throughout the brain, rather than localized in one area, which may be part of the reason older adults retain musical information longer and recall musical memories much more clearly than nonmusical memories. Studies consistently indicate that those living with dementia and/or cognitive decline show strong emotional reactions to music. Music can also elicit increased attention, increased socialization and engagement, increased reality orientation, stronger self-esteem and identity, better responses during reminiscence discussions, increased verbal responses, and decreased wandering and agitation. Given the important part music plays throughout the entirety of life, it makes sense that the need for and response to music would remain strong through the end of life as well.

As dementia, cognitive decline, and memory loss progress, loved ones can lose the ability to carry on a conversation, express needs, wants, and desires, and become increasingly frustrated and agitated. Additionally, as memories fade, so does a strong sense of personal identity and security. When unable to connect with those around them and unable to connect to their past and identity, loved ones can become increasingly isolated, anxious, and depressed. Music helps individuals to access their memories and their identities, and its familiarity provides a sense of comfort and security. Hans Christian Andersen once said, "When words fail, music speaks." Music allows individuals to not only reconnect with their memories, but also to connect with those around them, without the need for words. It not only has the ability to convey emotions and share what can be difficult to describe in words, it is an emotional outlet that does not require verbal or cognitive processing. Music can be the tool to help your loved one express his or her feelings and the resource to provide consistent engagement, comfort, socialization, and emotional release.

TIPS AND STRATEGIES FOR USING MUSIC EFFECTIVELY

It can be intimidating to use music with someone you care about, especially if you do not have any musical training or experience. It is easy to be overwhelmed by the quantity of music to choose from, especially when using music from another generation. Some people are not comfortable hearing the sound of their own voice and the thought of having to sing makes them uneasy. Many people love listening to music on their own, but have no idea where to start when contemplating how to share music with a loved one, especially someone whose musical tastes vary widely from their own. It is not necessary to sing with your loved one if it makes you uncomfortable. He or she can benefit from sharing music with you in other ways. Furthermore, choosing and sharing music can be much easier than you think with a few simple tips and strategies. If you are not familiar with the music you plan to use, listen to the recording before you share it. Most importantly, remember the music is present to help facilitate a pleasant experience for both of you, so go in with no expectations other than enjoying music with someone you care about. Keep an open mind; you never know when you will make a musical connection with your loved one.

Choosing appropriate and preferred music is key to effectively using music with your loved one. While this task may seem challenging, especially if your loved one has difficulty expressing opinions or recalling favorite genres or artists, this book is designed to make this process as easy as possible. Choosing music and creating playlists will be covered extensively in the next section, "How to Make the Most of This Book" on page 11, but there are a few basic strategies to keep in mind.

Research recommends selecting music that was popular when your loved one was in his or her late teens and/or early twenties. Don't be afraid of using a trial and error approach to see what he or she responds to the most, keeping in mind that responses can vary greatly from day to day. Remember too that some music may not be appropriate. For example, love songs may be challenging for someone whose spouse has recently passed away, and "Amazing Grace" may hold comfort for some individuals, while for others it is a strong reminder of a recent funeral. Please refer to "Additional Considerations and Resources" on page 13 for further guidance.

Once you have selected the music, consider the setting you will use for listening. Ideally, look for a space where your loved one is most comfortable, somewhere that can provide privacy and familiarity and has minimal distractions. Use a device that contains or is connected to speakers such as a laptop, phone, tablet, or CD player. This will maximize and enhance engagement between you and your loved one. Do not use headphones as they tend to isolate the listener, rather than encourage a shared experience. When testing your equipment always be mindful of the volume. It is better to start out at a softer volume and increase as needed rather than to start too loudly. Starting at a loud volume can create a startle response. This could cause an adverse reaction that often is more severe in individuals with cognitive decline and/or dementia.

Once you are settled, comfortable, and have pressed play, observe your loved one as you listen together and take notice of any movement or engagement on his or her part. As your loved one is listening, try to mirror his or her facial expressions and movements. While listening to the music, encourage any spontaneous movement your loved one displays. Simple actions you could encourage your loved one to complete along with the beat include: tapping toes, clapping hands, swaying side to side, humming or singing along with the recording, or holding your loved one's hands to help him or her dance along.

After listening, consider asking your loved one a question or two about the song. If he or she does not have much to say, do not consider it a failure, simply move on to enjoying another song together. While engaging in movement and discussion with your loved one, speak in a clear and steady tone and be sure to pause between statements, questions, and/or directions. Individuals living with cognitive decline and/or dementia typically have a slower response and reaction time. Providing a pause will allow them time to process what was said and give them time to respond, which will lead to a more positive overall experience.

SUMMARY OF KEY STEPS

- **Select Preferred Music**
- **Choose a Comfortable Listening Space with Minimal Distractions**
- **Set Up and Make Sure Listening Devices Are Working**
- **Start the Music at a Low Volume, Increase Volume as Needed**
- **Observe Reactions and Encourage Movement with the Music**
- **Ask Follow-Up Questions About the Song; Give Additional Prompts as Needed**

HOW TO MAKE THE MOST OF THIS BOOK

This book is designed to be a practical guide on how to effectively use music with older adults who are experiencing cognitive decline and/or memory loss, regardless of whether they have a dementia diagnosis or how mild or severe those challenges may be. **Part Two** *of this book contains extensive playlists of recommended music to listen to and enjoy.* **Part Three** *is a series of engaged listening discussions based on popular songs and holidays. The information below will help you make the most of this book.*

Sharing music gives your loved one additional ways to interact and socialize with his or her peers and caregivers and can provide a sense of belonging. When tailoring a playlist to support the needs and interests of your loved one, keep in mind an individual's musical preferences can be influenced by a variety of factors. Research suggests that influences on musical preferences may include educational background, community, culture, and whether or not a person has received musical instruction or training. It is important to gather as much information as possible in regards to your loved one's musical preferences. This information will be invaluable when creating a music playlist and the overall process will be easier than just guessing. The best source for information about your loved one's musical preferences is your loved one. If they are able to provide answers, ask as many music-related questions as you can think of, such as:

- What kind of music do you enjoy? (Prompt with examples as needed, such as Country, Blues, Jazz, Folk, Hymns, Musicals, Classical, Patriotic, Rock and Roll, Big Band, Pop, etc.)

- Do you have any specific artists or bands that you enjoy?

- What are your favorite songs?

For more ideas, see the form on page 16. If your loved one is not able to answer these questions, keep in mind that research suggests older adults prefer music that was popular during their young adult years, typically when they were between the ages of 18 and 25. Try researching the top hits from this time in their life or simply refer to the decade-based playlists in **Part Two** of this book. This will give you a strong starting point, especially if you are unable to obtain any information regarding your loved one's musical preferences.

Some research suggests that people will also have a strong response to music that was popular during their early childhood. Typically this would include their parents' or guardians' favorite music or music that was sung to them while growing up. This may be beneficial or special because it can remind your loved one of his or her family and friends from childhood. Often, those memories and associations remain strong as he or she ages. Remember, your loved one's musical preferences may change from day to day. Their cognitive decline and/or dementia may affect how they are feeling as well as how they perceive their age in any given moment. At times they may think they are a child again, or taking care of their children, or see themselves at their present age. When this happens, it is best to meet your loved one in the moment. Since each individual's relationship to music is personal, it can be difficult to classify music based on mood and emotion. It is important to keep in mind that music that is relaxing or energizing to one person may not have the same effect on someone else. The detailed decade and genre playlists available in **Part Two** will help guide your listening. You may use them in their entirety or pick and choose based on the feedback you receive. If your loved one requests or prefers songs or genres not covered in this book, feel free to use them.

You can find a multitude of available resources to share and listen to recorded music. You are encouraged to use whichever source you are most comfortable with, including digital media, CDs, or even records. iTunes, Amazon Music, Spotify, and even YouTube are places you might obtain music online and are easy to use with smartphones, laptops, tablets, and digital music players.

Part Three of this book contains more than 100 engaged listening discussions. These detailed outlines will walk you through how to take a shared musical experience beyond simply listening and provide ideas for movement, pictures/images to reference, and most importantly, discussion questions. These are meant to encourage greater interaction between you and your loved one and help you use the power of music to guide him or her through recalling and sharing memories and ideas.

These discussion outlines can be used in any order. Choose what will be most meaningful for your loved one in the moment. You should feel free to modify or omit suggestions and to encourage spontaneous conversation as well. When following movement suggestions, keep in mind that your loved one will be more likely to move along with the music if he or she sees you moving as well, and that verbal encouragement will help too. When engaging in discussion, start with more open-ended questions. If your loved one is struggling with a response, or if his or her response is limited or generalized, then give additional prompts or suggestions as needed. Oftentimes, you may get vague or general responses such as "everything" or "too many to say" in response to open-ended questions such as "What is something that brings you happiness?" or "What are the qualities you look for in a friend?" These vague responses can indicate your loved one is struggling to provide details. Additional prompts, suggestions, or follow-up questions will help him or her focus their thoughts. For each engaged listening discussion additional prompts, follow up questions, and answers are included in parentheses for you to use as needed. Most importantly, these discussions are meant to be enjoyable for both of you, so go with what feels most comfortable and have fun.

ADDITIONAL CONSIDERATIONS AND RESOURCES

Listening to music is both an emotional experience and a social experience. It may not always illicit happy or positive memories and feelings. As mentioned earlier, an individual may have personal associations, connections, and emotions to any given song.

If your loved one becomes upset or tearful during a particular song, it does not always imply a negative experience. However, it is important to be aware that negative associations and experiences can happen while listening to music. Ignoring a negative reaction is never the answer.

Acknowledging and validating those feelings can provide support and understanding for both you and your loved one. If you do not feel comfortable supporting your loved one through the potential emotional ups and downs of the music-listening experience, or if you observe your loved one becoming frequently tearful, aggressive, acting out, or displaying behaviors that are distressing, these concerns should be brought to a music therapist, counselor, doctor, social worker, or another healthcare professional in your area. It is crucial to recognize when those negative emotional reactions are representative of a deeper issue, are more intense, occur with greater frequency, or any other indication that your loved one needs help emotionally processing beyond what you can provide. In these cases, seek professional help. A selection of resources is provided on the following pages to help you navigate the changing needs of your loved one. These resources are not intended as a substitute for treatment.

The Certification Board for Music Therapists

www.cbmt.org

"CBMT is the only organization to certify music therapists to practice music therapy nationally. Its MT-BC program has been fully accredited by the National Commission for Certifying Agencies. (NCCA) since 1986." —WWW.CBMT.ORG

This website provides a quick way to search for music therapists in your area or to check an individual's music therapy credentials.

American Music Therapy Association

www.musictherapy.org

"AMTA's purpose is the progressive development of the therapeutic use of music in rehabilitation, special education, and community settings. Predecessors, unified in 1998, included the National Association for Music Therapy founded in 1950 and the American Association for Music Therapy founded in 1971. AMTA is committed to the advancement of education, training, professional standards, credentials, and research in support of the music therapy profession." —WWW.MUSICTHERAPY.ORG

This is a great resource to learn more about music therapy. You can also search for a music therapist using the online directory. However, this will only list the music therapists who are current members of AMTA.

Alzheimer's Association

www.alz.org

"Formed in 1980, the Alzheimer's Association advances research to end Alzheimer's and dementia while enhancing care for those living with the disease." —WWW.ALZ.ORG

This resource gives information about Alzheimer's disease and other types of dementia. It provides symptoms and stages, current treatments and research, and what to do if you or a loved one has been diagnosed with Alzheimer's disease. It includes caregiving tips and ways to get involved. This organization has a wealth of information and is a helpful resource both for those who have been diagnosed and those caring for them.

AARP Caregiving Resource Center

www.aarp.org/home-family/caregiving

This resource is significant because it is 100% dedicated to providing education and support to caregivers. Here, you can find information on benefits and insurance, legal and financial information, caring for yourself, providing care, senior housing, and end of life care.

ElderSong Publications, Inc.

www.eldersong.com

This resource will be helpful if you are looking for more creative ways to interact with your loved one. ElderSong strives to provide "creative activity materials for older adults." Here, you will be able to find books, CDs, DVDs, games, and activity ideas.

The Validation Breakthrough: Simple Techniques for Communication with People with Alzheimer's and Other Dementias, 3rd Edition
by Naomi Feil; 1989/2012

This book details how to use validation to more effectively communicate and redirect challenging behaviors in older adults living with Alzheimer's-type dementia. The techniques described focus on validating the feelings being expressed, rather than immediately correcting disorientation. Clearly described and easy to apply, these techniques can be used by professional and family caregivers to focus on understanding the behaviors and emotions expressed.

Untangling Alzheimer's: The Guide for Families and Professionals (A Conversation in Caregiving)
by Tam Cummings, PhD, Gerontologist; 2013

In this book, Tam Cummings explains Alzheimer's disease and other forms of dementia in terms everyone can understand. She provides and describes the progression of the disease, communication techniques, techniques to address caregiver stress, ways to work with and track combative behaviors, and how to share this information with your doctor. It also includes information about end of life care and support.

Creating Moments of Joy Along the Alzheimer's Journey: A Guide for Families and Caregivers, 5th Edition
by Jolene Brackey; first published in 1999

Jolene Brackey's main focus in this book is how you can create moments of joy for someone living with Alzheimer's disease and other types of dementia. "We are not able to create perfectly wonderful days for people with dementia or Alzheimer's, but we can create perfectly wonderful moments." This book is a great resource to help you focus on the best way to create these moments.

Teepa Snow
www.teepasnow.com

Teepa Snow is one of the leaders in dementia education and training. Her website provides a variety of resources including book recommendations, blogs and online reading, and information for kids and teens who have a loved one living with dementia. In addition to the variety of resources, this website also provides helpful tips and strategies to use when caring for someone living with dementia.

MUSICAL PREFERENCES QUESTIONNAIRE

Use this form to gather and organize as much information as you can about your loved one's musical preferences. This information can be obtained by asking your loved one directly, consulting with friends, family members, and caregivers, and by noting his or her personal history.

_____   _____
NAME   DATE OF BIRTH

FAVORITE GENRES/STYLES OF MUSIC:
(ex. Blues, Jazz, Folk, Hymns, Musicals, Classical, Country, Patriotic, Rock and Roll, Big Band, Pop)

FAVORITE ARTISTS OR BANDS:

KNOWN FAVORITE SONGS:

RELIGIOUS AFFILIATION AND INVOLVEMENT:

MILITARY SERVICE AND INVOLVEMENT:

INSTRUMENTS PLAYED/PARTICIPATION IN BAND OR CHOIR:

HOBBIES AND INTERESTS:

Recommended
Playlists

NOTES ON PART TWO

*The following playlists were developed based on an original research survey of music therapists, a review of **Billboard** charts, and the best therapeutic judgment of the authors. They are by no means comprehensive but are intended to serve as a thorough sampling for each category. The better (or more specific) responses you receive from your loved one regarding his or her preferred music, the better equipped you will be to provide music that is representative of his or her tastes.*

These playlists are a solid and proven successful starting place and serve as a guide for those working with a loved one unable to recall or communicate preferences. For assistance in determining which playlists will be most beneficial for your loved one, please refer to **Part One**. Feel free to pick and choose from each playlist, always observing your loved one's responses and using those responses to guide future selections. Songs that are included in **Part Three**, Engaged Listening Discussions, are denoted by ♪.

There are a variety of places to obtain music when building a playlist for your loved one, whether you are buying the song outright on iTunes or Amazon, using a subscription service such as Spotify, using music from an actual physical recording, or even accessing a song on YouTube. Considering the plethora of versions available for many of the suggested songs, and because digital offerings can change relatively rapidly, two to three recommended artists are listed for every song that has more than one popular artist. Many songs, especially those from earlier years, have been recorded by numerous artists over several decades and the artists listed there are simply suggestions. If your loved one has a preferred version that is not listed, you are encouraged to share that recording. Songs were placed on playlists based on when they were the among the biggest hits of the time and where they make the most sense musically.

For "Hymns and Spirituals," "Patriotic Music," and "Popular Christmas Classics," there are many well-known versions of each song available and the listener's preference is recommended.

TIMELESS CLASSICS

♪ **ALEXANDER'S RAGTIME BAND**: *Arthur Collins, The Andrews Sisters*

THE BAND PLAYED ON: *Guy Lombardo*

♪ **BILL BAILEY, WON'T YOU PLEASE COME HOME**: *Jimmy Durante, Patsy Cline*

BY THE LIGHT OF THE SILVERY MOON: *Mitch Miller, Doris Day*

♪ **DAISY BELL (BICYCLE BUILT FOR TWO)**: *Nat King Cole, Dinah Shore*

FOR ME AND MY GAL: *Judy Garland & Gene Kelly*

GOODNIGHT, IRENE: *Lead Belly, The Weavers*

GOODNIGHT, LADIES: *Crown Records Studio Group*

HAIL, HAIL, THE GANG'S ALL HERE: *Nat Shilkret & the Victor Orchestra*

I'M FOREVER BLOWING BUBBLES: *Ben Selvin & His Novelty Orchestra, Doris Day & Jack Smith*

IN MY MERRY OLDSMOBILE: *Billy Murray, Jo Stafford*

♪ **IN THE GOOD OLD SUMMERTIME**: *Nat King Cole*

♪ **LET ME CALL YOU SWEETHEART**: *The Peerless Quartet, Bing Crosby*

MEET ME IN ST. LOUIS: *Judy Garland*

♪ **MOONLIGHT BAY**: *The American Quartet, Doris Day*

PACK UP YOUR TROUBLES IN YOUR OLD KIT-BAG, AND SMILE, SMILE, SMILE:
Dick Haymes & the Andrews Sisters

PEG O' MY HEART: *Charles Harrison, Mitch Miller*

PRETTY BABY: *Al Jolson, Dean Martin*

♪ **SCHOOL DAYS (WHEN WE WERE A COUPLE OF KIDS)**: *Byron Harlan, Tiny Tim*

♪ **SHINE ON, HARVEST MOON**: *Ada Jones & Billy Murray, Bing Crosby & Rosemary Clooney*

THE SIDEWALKS OF NEW YORK: *Bob Hope*

♪ **TAKE ME OUT TO THE BALLGAME**: *Gene Kelly, Wurlitzer Pipe Organ (instrumental)*

THERE IS A TAVERN IN THE TOWN: *Rudy Vallee*

TILL WE MEET AGAIN: *Doris Day*

WHEN IRISH EYES ARE SMILING: *Bing Crosby*

WHEN YOU WORE A TULIP AND I WORE A BIG RED ROSE: *Judy Garland, David Rose & Gene Kelly*

SONGS OF THE 1920s

AIN'T SHE SWEET: *Gene Austin*

AIN'T WE GOT FUN: *Doris Day (1953) Peggy Lee (1959)*

ALWAYS: *Nick Lucas, Henry Burr*

APRIL SHOWERS: *Al Jolson*

BABY FACE: *Jan Garber & His Orchestra*

♪ **BLUE SKIES:** *Belle Baker, Ben Selvin, Al Jolson*

♪ **BUTTON UP YOUR OVERCOAT:** *Ruth Etting, Helen Kane*

♪ **BYE BYE BLACKBIRD:** *Sam Lanin's Dance Orchestra, Nick Lucas, Gene Austin*

CAROLINA IN THE MORNING: *Al Jolson, Marion Harris*

THE CHARLESTON: *Paul Whiteman & His Orchestra (instrumental)*

HAPPY DAYS ARE HERE AGAIN: *Leo Reisman & His Orchestra, Ben Selvin & His Orchestra*

♪ **HAS ANYBODY SEEN MY GAL? (FIVE FOOT TWO, EYES OF BLUE):** *California Ramblers*

HONEYSUCKLE ROSE: *Fats Waller*

I WANNA BE LOVED BY YOU: *Helen Kane*

♪ **I'M LOOKING OVER A FOUR LEAF CLOVER:** *Nick Lucas*

(I'LL BE WITH YOU) IN APPLE BLOSSOM TIME: *Nora Bayes, The Andrews Sisters (1941)*

IT HAD TO BE YOU: *Paul Whiteman & His Orchestra*

MAKIN' WHOOPEE: *Eddie Cantor*

MY BLUE HEAVEN: *Gene Austin*

MY BUDDY: *Henry Burr*

PINETOP'S BOOGIE WOOGIE: *Pinetop Smith*

SAINT LOUIS BLUES: *Bessie Smith & Louis Armstrong*

SHOW ME THE WAY TO GO HOME: *Frank Crumit, The California Ramblers*

♪ **SIDE BY SIDE:** *Cliff Edwards, Nick Lucas*

STARDUST: *Louis Armstrong, Nat King Cole*

SWANEE: *Al Jolson*

SWEET GEORGIA BROWN: *Cab Calloway, Ben Bernie (instrumental)*

TEA FOR TWO: *Art Tatum, Fats Waller*

♪ **TIPTOE THROUGH THE TULIPS:** *Nick Lucas*

WHEN THE RED, RED ROBIN (COMES BOB, BOB, BOBBIN' ALONG): *Al Jolson*

♪ **YES SIR, THAT'S MY BABY:** *Ace Brigode, Eddie Cantor (1930)*

♪ **YES! WE HAVE NO BANANAS:** *Eddie Cantor, Billy Jones & Orchestra*

SONGS OF THE 1930s

A-TISKET, A-TASKET: *Ella Fitzgerald*

ALL OF ME: *Ruth Etting*

BACK IN THE SADDLE AGAIN: *Gene Autry*

♪ **BEER BARREL POLKA:** *Will Glahe (instrumental), Frank Yankovic & Yanks*

BEGIN THE BEGUINE: *Artie Shaw & His Orchestra*

BEI MIR BIST DU SCHOEN: *The Andrews Sisters, Benny Goodman*

BOOGIE WOOGIE: *Tommy Dorsey & His Orchestra*

CHEEK TO CHEEK: *Fred Astaire*

♪ **GOD BLESS AMERICA:** *Kate Smith*

HEART AND SOUL: *Larry Clinton & His Orchestra*

♪ **I GOT RHYTHM:** *Ethel Merman, Ella Fitzgerald, Judy Garland*

I'M GONNA SIT RIGHT DOWN AND WRITE MYSELF A LETTER: *Fats Waller*

I'M IN THE MOOD FOR LOVE: *Frances Langford, Louis Armstrong*

I'VE GOT MY LOVE TO KEEP ME WARM: *Alice Faye, Billie Holiday*

IT DON'T MEAN A THING (IF IT AIN'T GOT THAT SWING): *Duke Ellington, Louis Armstrong*

IT'S ONLY A PAPER MOON: *Paul Whiteman & His Orchestra, Ella Fitzgerald, Nat King Cole Trio*

LET'S CALL THE WHOLE THING OFF: *Fred Astaire & Ginger Rogers*

MINNIE THE MOOCHER: *Cab Calloway & His Orchestra*

NIGHT AND DAY: *Fred Astaire, Frank Sinatra (1942)*

♪ **ON THE GOOD SHIP LOLLIPOP:** *Shirley Temple*

ON THE SUNNY SIDE OF THE STREET: *Tommy Dorsey & His Orchestra (instrumental), Louis Armstrong*

♪ **(SOMEWHERE) OVER THE RAINBOW:** *Judy Garland*

PENNIES FROM HEAVEN: *Bing Crosby*

PUTTIN' ON THE RITZ: *Fred Astaire*

SING, SING, SING (WITH A SWING): *Benny Goodman (instrumental)*

STORMY WEATHER: *Ethel Waters, Lena Horne, Billie Holiday*

♪ **SUMMERTIME:** *Ella Fitzgerald & Louis Armstrong, Billie Holiday*

THANKS FOR THE MEMORY: *Bob Hope*

♪ **THE WAY YOU LOOK TONIGHT:** *Fred Astaire, Bing Crosby & Dixi Lee, Frank Sinatra (1955)*

WHEN IT'S SPRINGTIME IN THE ROCKIES: *Gene Autry*

♪ **WHEN THE SAINTS GO MARCHING IN:** *Louis Armstrong & His Orchestra*

WHEN YOU'RE SMILING: *Louis Armstrong*

WHISTLE WHILE YOU WORK: *Adriana Caselotti*

SONGS OF THE 1940s

A STRING OF PEARLS: *Glenn Miller & His Orchestra (instrumental)*

ACCENTUATE THE POSITIVE: *Artie Shaw, Ella Fitzgerald, Bing Crosby & the Andrews Sisters*

♪ **AS TIME GOES BY**: *Dooley Wilson*

AUTUMN LEAVES : *Johnny Mercer, Jo Stafford, Roger Williams (1955 instrumental)*

THE BELLS OF ST. MARY'S: *Bing Crosby*

BOOGIE WOOGIE BUGLE BOY: *The Andrews Sisters*

BUTTONS AND BOWS: *Dinah Shore*

♪ **CHATTANOOGA CHOO CHOO**: *The Glenn Miller Orchestra*

DEEP IN THE HEART OF TEXAS: *Perry Como with Ted Weems & His Orchestra, Gene Autry*

DON'T FENCE ME IN: *Roy Rogers, Bing Crosby & The Andrews Sisters*

♪ **DON'T SIT UNDER THE APPLE TREE (WITH ANYONE ELSE BUT ME)**: *Glenn Miller, The Andrews Sisters*

IF I LOVED YOU: *Jan Clayton & John Raitt, Gordon MacRae & Shirley Jones (1956)*

I'LL BE SEEING YOU: *Bing Crosby, Rosemary Clooney*

♪ **I'M LOOKING OVER A FOUR LEAF CLOVER**: *Art Mooney*

IN THE MOOD: *Glenn Miller (instrumental)*

IT HAD TO BE YOU: *Frank Sinatra, Dinah Shore*

IT MIGHT AS WELL BE SPRING: *Dick Haymes*

JINGLE JANGLE JINGLE: *Kay Kyser*

♪ **OH, WHAT A BEAUTIFUL MORNIN'**: *Alfred Drake, Gordon MacRae (1955)*

OLD DEVIL MOON: *Ella Logan & Donald Richards, Frank Sinatra (1956)*

PAPER DOLL: *The Mills Brothers*

♪ **(GHOST) RIDERS IN THE SKY: A COWBOY LEGEND**: *Vaughn Monroe*

♪ **(GET YOUR KICKS ON) ROUTE 66**: *Nat King Cole, Bing Crosby & The Andrews Sisters*

♪ **SENTIMENTAL JOURNEY**: *Doris Day*

SOME ENCHANTED EVENING: *Ezio Pinza, Perry Como*

SWINGING ON A STAR: *Bing Crosby*

♪ **THIS LAND IS YOUR LAND**: *Woody Guthrie*

♪ **WHEN YOU WISH UPON A STAR**: *Cliff Edwards*

♪ **YOU ARE MY SUNSHINE**: *Jimmie Davis*

♪ **ZIP-A-DEE-DOO-DAH**: *Frank Baskett, Johnny Mercer*

SONGS OF THE 1950s

ALL I HAVE TO DO IS DREAM: *The Everly Brothers*

THE BALLAD OF DAVY CROCKETT: *The Wellingtons, Bill Hayes*

BLUE MOON: *The Marcels, Elvis Presley*

BLUEBERRY HILL: *Fats Domino*

CHANTILLY LACE: *The Big Bopper*

♪ **EDELWEISS:** *Theodore Bikel, Bill Lee & Charmain Carr (1965)*

FEVER: *Peggy Lee*

GOODNITE, SWEETHEART, GOODNITE: *The Spaniels, McGuire Sisters*

HARBOR LIGHTS: *Sammy Kaye & His Orchestra, The Platters (1960)*

HEARTBREAK HOTEL: *Elvis Presley*

♪ **HEY, GOOD LOOKIN':** *Hank Williams*

♪ **HOUND DOG:** *Elvis Presley*

♪ **I COULD HAVE DANCED ALL NIGHT:** *Julie Andrews, Marni Nixon (1964)*

I WALK THE LINE: *Johnny Cash*

IF I KNEW YOU WERE COMIN' I'D'VE BAKED A CAKE: *Eileen Barton*

♪ **IN THE STILL OF THE NIGHT:** *The Five Satins*

♪ **JAMBALAYA (ON THE BAYOU):** *Hank Williams*

♪ **JOHNNY B. GOODE:** *Chuck Berry*

LA BAMBA: *Ritchie Valens*

♪ **LOVE ME TENDER:** *Elvis Presley*

MACK THE KNIFE: *Bobby Darrin*

MUSIC! MUSIC! MUSIC!: *Teresa Brewer*

♪ **MY FAVORITE THINGS:** *Julie Andrews (1965)*

♪ **QUE SERA, SERA (WHATEVER WILL BE, WILL BE):** *Doris Day*

♪ **ROCK AROUND THE CLOCK:** *Bill Haley & His Comets*

♪ **SHAKE, RATTLE AND ROLL:** *Joe Turner, Bill Haley & His Comets*

♪ **SINGIN' IN THE RAIN:** *Gene Kelley*

♪ **SIXTEEN TONS:** *Tennessee Ernie Ford*

♪ **TENNESSEE WALTZ:** *Patti Page*

♪ **(HOW MUCH IS) THAT DOGGIE IN THE WINDOW?:** *Patti Page*

THAT'S AMORE: *Dean Martin*

VAYA CON DIOS: *Les Paul & Mary Ford*

SONGS OF THE 1960s

THE 59TH STREET BRIDGE SONG (FEELIN' GROOVY): *Simon & Garfunkel*
AIN'T NO MOUNTAIN HIGH ENOUGH: *Marvin Gaye & Tami Terrell, Diana Ross (1970)*
AT LAST: *Etta James*
BIG GIRLS DON'T CRY: *The Four Seasons*
BROWN EYED GIRL: *Van Morrison*
BUILD ME UP BUTTERCUP: *The Foundations*
CALIFORNIA DREAMIN': *The Mamas & The Papas*
CAN'T HELP FALLING IN LOVE: *Elvis Presley*
DO WAH DIDDY DIDDY: *Manfred Man*
(SITTIN' ON) THE DOCK OF THE BAY: *Ottis Redding*
♪ **DOWNTOWN:** *Petula Clark*
FLY ME TO THE MOON: *Peggy Lee, Frank Sinatra*
♪ **GEORGIA ON MY MIND:** *Ray Charles*
♪ **HERE COMES THE SUN:** *The Beatles*
HEY JUDE: *The Beatles*
I HEARD IT THROUGH THE GRAPEVINE: *Marvin Gaye*
♪ **I WANT TO HOLD YOUR HAND:** *The Beatles*
I'M A BELIEVER: *The Monkees*
♪ **ITSY BITSY TEENIE WEENIE YELLOW POLKA DOT BIKINI:** *Brian Hyland*
KING OF THE ROAD: *Roger Miller*
LET'S TWIST AGAIN: *Chubby Checker*
THE LOCO-MOTION: *Little Eva, Grand Funk Railroad (1974)*
♪ **MOON RIVER:** *Audrey Hepburn, Andy Williams*
♪ **MY GIRL:** *The Temptations*
MY WAY: *Frank Sinatra*
♪ **RING OF FIRE:** *Johnny Cash*
STAND BY ME: *Ben E. King*
♪ **SURFIN' SAFARI:** *The Beach Boys*
SWEET CAROLINE: *Neil Diamond*
THESE BOOTS ARE MADE FOR WALKIN': *Nancy Sinatra*
THE TWIST: *Chubby Checker*
UNCHAINED MELODY: *The Righteous Brothers*
♪ **WHAT A WONDERFUL WORLD:** *Louis Armstrong*
WILL YOU LOVE ME TOMORROW: *The Shirelles*
♪ **WITH A LITTLE HELP FROM MY FRIENDS:** *The Beatles, Joe Cocker*
♪ **YELLOW SUBMARINE:** *The Beatles*
YOU CAN'T ALWAYS GET WHAT YOU WANT: *The Rolling Stones*
♪ **YOU CAN'T HURRY LOVE:** *The Supremes*

SONGS OF THE 1970s

AMERICAN PIE: *Don McLean*

BAD, BAD LEROY BROWN: *Jim Croce*

♪ BRIDGE OVER TROUBLED WATER: *Simon & Garfunkel*

CAT'S IN THE CRADLE: *Harry Chapin*

DANCING QUEEN: *ABBA*

DON'T GO BREAKING MY HEART: *Elton John & Kiki Dee*

HOTEL CALIFORNIA: *Eagles*

♪ I CAN SEE CLEARLY NOW: *Johnny Nash*

I WILL SURVIVE: *Gloria Gaynor*

I'LL BE THERE: *Jackson 5*

IMAGINE: *John Lennon*

JOY TO THE WORLD: *Three Dog Night*

♪ LEAN ON ME: *Bill Withers*

♪ LET IT BE: *The Beatles*

LOVE WILL KEEP US TOGETHER: *Captain & Tennille*

MAGGIE MAY: *Rod Stewart*

ME AND BOBBY MCGEE: *Janis Joplin*

MIDNIGHT TRAIN TO GEORGIA: *Gladys Knight & the Pips*

RAINDROPS KEEP FALLIN' ON MY HEAD: *B.J. Thomas*

STAIRWAY TO HEAVEN: *Led Zeppelin*

STAYIN' ALIVE: *Bee Gees*

♪ SUNSHINE ON MY SHOULDERS: *John Denver*

SWEET HOME ALABAMA: *Lynyrd Skynyrd*

♪ THEME FROM NEW YORK, NEW YORK: *Liza Minnelli, Frank Sinatra*

TIE A YELLOW RIBBON ROUND THE OLE OAK TREE: *Tony Orlando & Dawn*

TIME IN A BOTTLE: *Jim Croce*

TOP OF THE WORLD: *The Carpenters*

THE WAY WE WERE: *Barbra Streisand*

WE ARE FAMILY: *Sister Sledge*

WONDERFUL TONIGHT: *Eric Clapton*

Y.M.C.A.: *Village People*

YOU ARE THE SUNSHINE OF MY LIFE: *Stevie Wonder*

YOU'VE GOT A FRIEND: *Carole King, James Taylor*

BROADWAY MUSICALS

A BUSHEL AND A PECK from *Guys and Dolls*: Vivian Blaine, Perry Como & Betty Hutton, Doris Day

ALL THAT JAZZ from *Chicago*: Chita Rivera

ANOTHER OP'NIN; ANOTHER SHOW from *Kiss Me Kate*: Broadway Cast Recording

♪ **ANYTHING YOU CAN DO** from *Annie Get Your Gun*: Ethel Merman & Ray Middleton, Betty Hutton & Howard Keel

BEING ALIVE from *Company*: Dean Jones

CABARET from *Cabaret*: Liza Minnelli

CONSIDER YOURSELF from *Oliver!*: Broadway Cast Recording

DO-RE-MI from *The Sound of Music*: Mary Martin, Julie Andrews

DON'T CRY FOR ME ARGENTINA from *Evita*: Julie Covington, Elaine Paige

♪ **EDELWEISS** from *The Sound of Music*: Theodore Bikel, Bill Lee & Charmain Carr

♪ **GETTING TO KNOW YOU** from *The King and I*: Gertrude Lawrence, Marni Nixon

GIVE MY REGARDS TO BROADWAY from *Little Johnny Jones/George M!*: George M. Cohan, James Cagney

♪ **HELLO, DOLLY!** from *Hello Dolly!*: Carol Channing, Barbra Streisand, Louis Armstrong

♪ **I COULD HAVE DANCED ALL NIGHT** from *My Fair Lady*: Julie Andrews, Marni Nixon

I FEEL PRETTY from *West Side Story*: Carol Lawrence, Marni Nixon

♪ **I GOT RHYTHM** from *Girl Crazy/An American in Paris*: Ethel Merman, Judy Garland, Gene Kelly

IF I LOVED YOU from *Carousel*: Jan Clayton & John Raitt, Gordon MacRae & Shirley Jones

♪ **I'M GONNA WASH THAT MAN RIGHT OUTA MY HAIR** from *South Pacific*: Mary Martin, Mitzi Gaynor

THE IMPOSSIBLE DREAM (THE QUEST) from *Man of La Mancha*: Richard Kiley, Andy Williams

LULLABY OF BROADWAY: Doris Day

MARIA from *West Side Story*: Larry Kert, Jimmy Bryant

♪ **OH, WHAT A BEAUTIFUL MORNIN'** from *Oklahoma!*: Alfred Drake, Gordon MacRae

OKLAHOMA from *Oklahoma!*: Jay Blackton, Gordon MacRae

ONE from *A Chorus Line*: Broadway Cast Recording

PEOPLE from *Funny Girl*: Barbra Streisand

PUT ON A HAPPY FACE from *Bye Bye Birdie*: Charles Strouse, Dick Van Dyke

SEND IN THE CLOWNS from *A Little Night Music*: Glynis Johns, Judy Collins

SEVENTY-SIX TROMBONES from *The Music Man*: Robert Preston

SOME ENCHANTED EVENING from *South Pacific*: Ezio Penza, Giorgio Tozzi

THE SOUND OF MUSIC from *The Sound of Music*: Mary Martin, Julie Andrews

♪ **SUNRISE, SUNSET** from *Fiddler on the Roof*: Zero Mostel & Maria Karnilova, Topol & Norma Crane

THERE'S NO BUSINESS LIKE SHOW BUSINESS from *Annie Get Your Gun*: Ethel Merman & Ray Middleton, Betty Hutton & Howard Keel

TOMORROW from *Annie*: Andrea McArdle

ROCK & ROLL

♪ **ALL SHOOK UP:** *Elvis Presley*
AT THE HOP: *Danny & the Juniors*
BLUE SUEDE SHOES: *Elvis Presley, Carl Perkins*
THE BOOK OF LOVE: *The Monotones*
BYE BYE LOVE: *The Everly Brothers, Simon & Garfunkel*
DUKE OF EARL: *Gene Chandler*
EARTH ANGEL: *The Penguins, Frankie Avalon*
EIGHT DAYS A WEEK: *The Beatles*
GOOD GOLLY, MISS MOLLY: *Little Richard*
GOOD VIBRATIONS: *The Beach Boys*
GREAT BALLS OF FIRE: *Jerry Lee Lewis*
♪ **HOUND DOG:** *Elvis Presley*
I GOT YOU (I FEEL GOOD): *James Brown*
♪ **I WANT TO HOLD YOUR HAND:** *The Beatles*
I'M A BELIEVER: *The Monkees*
♪ **IN THE STILL OF THE NIGHT:** *The Five Satins*
JAILHOUSE ROCK: *Elvis Presley*
♪ **JOHNNY B. GOODE:** *Chuck Berry*
LA BAMBA: *Ritchie Valens*
LET'S TWIST AGAIN: *Chubby Checker*
LOVE POTION NO. 9: *The Clovers, The Searchers*
ONLY YOU (AND YOU ALONE): *The Platters*
PUT YOUR HEAD ON MY SHOULDER: *Paul Anka, The Lettermen*
ROCK AND ROLL MUSIC: *Chuck Berry*
♪ **ROCK AROUND THE CLOCK:** *Bill Haley & His Comets*
ROCK 'N' ROLL IS HERE TO STAY: *Danny & the Juniors, Sha Na Na*
ROCKIN' ROBIN: *Bobby Day, Michael Jackson*
SEE YOU LATER, ALLIGATOR: *Bill Haley & His Comets*
♪ **SHAKE, RATTLE AND ROLL:** *Joe Turner, Bill Haley & His Comets*
SH-BOOM: *The Chords*
SHOUT: *The Isley Brothers*
♪ **SUMMERTIME BLUES:** *Eddie Cochran*
♪ **THAT'LL BE THE DAY:** *Buddy Holly & the Crickets*
TUTTI FRUTTI: *Little Richard*
THE TWIST: *Chubby Checker*
TWIST AND SHOUT: *The Isley Brothers*
UP ON THE ROOF: *The Drifters*
WAKE UP LITTLE SUSIE: *The Everly Brothers*
WIPEOUT: *The Surfaris (instrumental)*
♪ **YAKETY YAK:** *The Coasters*

COUNTRY & WESTERN

ALWAYS ON MY MIND: *Brenda Lee, Elvis Presley, Willie Nelson*

BACK IN THE SADDLE AGAIN: *Gene Autry*

BUFFALO GALS: *Woody Guthrie, Pete Seeger*

COAL MINER'S DAUGHTER: *Loretta Lynn*

CRAZY: *Patsy Cline*

DADDY SANG BASS: *Johnny Cash*

DELTA DAWN: *Tanya Tucker, Helen Reddy*

THE DEVIL WENT DOWN TO GEORGIA: *Charlie Daniels Band*

DO YOU KNOW YOU ARE MY SUNSHINE: *The Statler Brothers*

DON'T FENCE ME IN: *Roy Rogers, Gene Autry, Bing Crosby & The Andrews Sisters*

FOLSOM PRISON BLUES: *Johnny Cash*

THE GAMBLER: *Kenny Rogers*

♪ **HAPPY TRAILS**: *Roy Rogers*

♪ **HEY, GOOD LOOKIN'**: *Hank Williams*

I SAW THE LIGHT: *Hank Williams*

I WALK THE LINE: *Johnny Cash*

I WILL ALWAYS LOVE YOU: *Dolly Parton, Whitney Houston*

IT WASN'T GOD WHO MADE HONKY TONK ANGELS: *Kitty Wells*

♪ **JAMBALAYA (ON THE BAYOU)**: *Hank Williams*

JINGLE JANGLE JINGLE: *Kay Kyser, Gene Autry*

JOLENE: *Dolly Parton*

KING OF THE ROAD: *Roger Miller*

LUCKENBACH, TEXAS (BACK TO THE BASICS OF LOVE): *Waylon Jennings*

MAMMAS DON'T LET YOUR BABIES GROW UP TO BE COWBOYS: *Ed Bruce, Waylon Jennings & Willie Nelson*

ON THE ROAD AGAIN: *Willie Nelson*

RHINESTONE COWBOY: *Glen Campbell*

♪ **(GHOST) RIDERS IN THE SKY: A COWBOY LEGEND**: *Vaughn Monroe*

♪ **RING OF FIRE**: *Johnny Cash*

ROCKY MOUNTAIN HIGH: *John Denver*

SAN ANTONIO ROSE: *Bob Wills & His Texas Playboys*

♪ **SIXTEEN TONS**: *Tennessee Ernie Ford*

♪ **TAKE ME HOME, COUNTRY ROADS**: *John Denver*

TAKE THIS JOB AND SHOVE IT: *Johnny Paycheck*

♪ **TENNESSEE WALTZ**: *Patti Page*

THANK GOD I'M A COUNTRY BOY: *John Denver*

THE WABASH CANNONBALL: *The Carter Family, Roy Acuff*

♪ **WALKIN' AFTER MIDNIGHT**: *Patsy Cline*

WHY BABY WHY: *George Jones, Red Sovine & Webb Pierce*

THE YELLOW ROSE OF TEXAS: *Mitch Miller, Ernest Tubb*

♪ **YOUR CHEATIN' HEART**: *Hank Williams*

CONTEMPORARY FOLK SONGS

ANNIE'S SONG: *John Denver*

BLOWIN' IN THE WIND: *Bob Dylan; Peter, Paul & Mary*

BOTH SIDES, NOW: *Joni Mitchell, Judy Collins*

CAT'S IN THE CRADLE: *Harry Chapin*

THE CIRCLE GAME: *Joni Mitchell*

CITY OF NEW ORLEANS: *Steve Goodman, Arlo Guthrie*

DEEP IN THE HEART OF TEXAS: *Perry Como with Ted Weems & His Orchestra, Gene Autry*

IF I HAD A HAMMER: *Pete Seeger; Peter, Paul & Mary; The Weavers*

♪**LEAVING ON A JET PLANE**: *Peter, Paul and Mary; John Denver*

MR. TAMBOURINE MAN: *Bob Dylan, The Byrds*

PUFF, THE MAGIC DRAGON: *Peter, Paul & Mary*

SCARBOROUGH FAIR: *Simon & Garfunkel*

SO LONG IT'S BEEN GOOD TO KNOW YUH: *Woody Guthrie, The Weavers*

THE SOUND OF SILENCE: *Simon & Garfunkel*

SUZANNE: *Leonard Cohen*

TEACH YOUR CHILDREN: *Crosby, Stills, Nash & Young*

♪**THIS LAND IS YOUR LAND**: *Woody Guthrie*

TOM DOOLEY: *The Kingston Trio*

TURN! TURN! TURN! (TO EVERYTHING THERE IS A SEASON): *The Byrds*

UNIVERSAL SOLDIER: *Buffy Sainte-Marie, Donovan*

WE SHALL OVERCOME: *Pete Seeger; Joan Baez; Peter, Paul & Mary*

WHERE HAVE ALL THE FLOWERS GONE?: *The Kingston Trio; Peter, Paul & Mary*

THE WRECK OF THE EDMUND FITZGERALD: *Gordon Lightfoot*

TRADITIONAL FOLK MUSIC

THE BALLAD OF JOHN HENRY: *Hobart Crabtree*

BILLY BOY: *Burl Ives, Gene Kelly*

BUFFALO GALS: *Pete Seeger, Woody Guthrie*

CAMPTOWN RACES: *Al Jolson, Pete Seeger*

CLEMENTINE: *Pete Seeger*

♪ **DANNY BOY:** *The Irish Tenors, Bing Crosby, Eva Cassidy*

DOWN IN THE VALLEY: *Pete Seeger & Johnny Cash*

♪ **HOME ON THE RANGE:** *Gene Autry, Roy Rogers*

♪ **I'VE BEEN WORKING ON THE RAILROAD:** *Pete Seeger, John Denver*

KEEP ON THE SUNNY SIDE: *The Carter Family*

LOW BRIDGE, EVERYBODY DOWN (THE ERIE CANAL SONG): *Lee Murdock, The Merry Macs*

MICHAEL, ROW THE BOAT ASHORE: *The Highway Men; Peter, Paul & Mary*

♪ **MY BONNIE LIES OVER THE OCEAN:** *Mitch Miller*

MY OLD KENTUCKY HOME: *Johnny Cash, Kate Smith*

OH SHENANDOAH: *Pete Seeger, Dale Warland Singers*

♪ **OH! SUSANNA:** *Pete Seeger*

OLD FOLKS AT HOME (SWANEE RIVER): *Paul Robeson*

ON TOP OF OLD SMOKEY: *Gene Autry, Kate Smith*

POLLY WOLLY DOODLE: *Burl Ives, Shirley Temple*

RED RIVER VALLEY: *Marty Robbins, Gene Autry*

ROW, ROW, ROW YOUR BOAT: *The Beach Boys*

♪ **SHE'LL BE COMING 'ROUND THE MOUNTAIN:** *Pete Seeger, Josh Abbott*

SIMPLE GIFTS: *Judy Collins, New York Philharmonic (instrumental)*

TURKEY IN THE STRAW: *Phil Rosenthal, Fiddle Fiddle Fiddle (instrumental)*

THE WATER IS WIDE: *James Taylor, Joan Baez, Eva Cassidy*

THE YELLOW ROSE OF TEXAS: *Mitch Miller, Ernest Tubb*

HYMNS & SPIRITUALS

A MIGHTY FORTRESS IS OUR GOD

♪ AMAZING GRACE

BLESSED ASSURANCE

COME THOU FOUNT OF EVERY BLESSING

DO LORD, REMEMBER ME

DOWN BY THE RIVERSIDE

DOWN IN THE RIVER TO PRAY

GO TELL IT ON THE MOUNTAIN

GREAT IS THY FAITHFULNESS

HE'S GOT THE WHOLE WORLD

HOLY, HOLY, HOLY!

♪ HOW GREAT THOU ART

I SAW THE LIGHT

I'LL FLY AWAY

♪ IN THE GARDEN

♪ IN THE SWEET BY AND BY

♪ IT IS WELL WITH MY SOUL

♪ JESUS LOVES ME

JOSHUA FIT THE BATTLE OF JERICHO

JUST A CLOSER WALK WITH THEE

MAKE ME A CHANNEL OF YOUR PEACE

NEARER, MY GOD, TO THEE

OH HAPPY DAY

THE OLD RUGGED CROSS

(GIVE ME THAT) OLD-TIME RELIGION

ON EAGLE'S WINGS

SEEK YE FIRST

SOON AND VERY SOON

SWING LOW, SWEET CHARIOT

THIS LITTLE LIGHT OF MINE

THE WAYFARING STRANGER

WERE YOU THERE (WHEN THEY CRUCIFIED MY LORD)

♪ WHAT A FRIEND WE HAVE IN JESUS

♪ WHEN THE SAINTS GO MARCHING IN

WILL THE CIRCLE BE UNBROKEN?

PATRIOTIC MUSIC

AMERICA THE BEAUTIFUL

ANCHORS AWEIGH *(United States Navy)*

THE ARMY GOES ROLLING ALONG/THE CAISSON SONG *(United States Army)*

THE BATTLE HYMN OF THE REPUBLIC

♪ GOD BLESS AMERICA

HAIL TO THE CHIEF

THE MARINES' HYMN *(United States Marines)*

MY COUNTRY 'TIS OF THEE (AMERICA)

SEMPER PARATUS *(United States Coast Guard)*

THE STARS AND STRIPES FOREVER

THE STAR-SPANGLED BANNER

♪ THIS LAND IS YOUR LAND

THE U.S. AIR FORCE (OFF WE GO...) *(United States Air Force)*

THE WASHINGTON POST MARCH

WHEN JOHNNY COMES MARCHING HOME

YANKEE DOODLE

THE YANKEE DOODLE BOY

YOU'RE A GRAND OLD FLAG

POPULAR CHRISTMAS CLASSICS

ANGELS WE HAVE HEARD ON HIGH

AWAY IN A MANGER

BLUE CHRISTMAS

THE CHRISTMAS SONG (CHESTNUTS ROASTING ON AN OPEN FIRE)

DECK THE HALLS

FELIZ NAVIDAD

FROSTY THE SNOWMAN

HARK! THE HERALD ANGELS SING

HERE COMES SANTA CLAUS (DOWN SANTA CLAUS LANE)

IT'S BEGINNING TO LOOK A LOT LIKE CHRISTMAS

JINGLE BELL ROCK

JINGLE BELLS

JOY TO THE WORLD

LET IT SNOW! LET IT SNOW! LET IT SNOW!

THE LITTLE DRUMMER BOY

O CHRISTMAS TREE (O TANNENBAUM)

O HOLY NIGHT

ROCKIN' AROUND THE CHRISTMAS TREE

RUDOLPH THE RED-NOSED REINDEER

SANTA CLAUS IS COMIN' TO TOWN

SILENT NIGHT

SILVER BELLS

WE WISH YOU A MERRY CHRISTMAS

WHITE CHRISTMAS

WINTER WONDERLAND

Part Three

Engaged
Listening
Discussions

NOTES ON PART THREE

The following engaged listening discussions are arranged alphabetically by song title, with a selection of holiday-themed discussions at the end. Feel free to pick and choose throughout this section, based on your loved one's interests, musical preferences, and religious beliefs.

These discussions are written as a guide to help you more meaningfully engage your loved one through music. It is okay to modify or omit movement suggestions and/or discussion questions. Keep in mind that your loved one will be more likely to move along with the music if he or she sees you moving as well; verbal encouragement will help too. After listening, engage in the meaningful discussion questions. Feel free to encourage spontaneous conversation with your loved one, even if it is not directly related to the question asked. During discussion, be sure to wait long enough after each question to provide your loved one with the time needed to process the question and share an answer. For more examples on how to meaningfully engage your loved one refer to **Part One**.

ALEXANDER'S RAGTIME BAND

SONG: *"Alexander's Ragtime Band"*
COMPOSERS/WRITERS: *Irving Berlin (writer)*
ARTIST(S): *Arthur Collins, The Andrews Sisters*
YEAR(S) RELEASED: *1911*

ADDITIONAL INFORMATION

"Alexander's Ragtime Band" was originally written as an instrumental piece in 1910, but it wasn't until Berlin re-wrote it with lyrics in 1911 that the song became a hit. Its popularity soared when Al Jolson performed the song. It is reported that 1.5 million copies of the song's sheet music sold during the first year and a half after its publication. Despite his fame as a songwriter, Berlin was unable to read or write music and he relied on "musical secretaries" to write down the melodies he composed.

ENGAGED LISTENING

Encourage your loved one to move along with you as you listen together. Suggested movements to model include: tap toes side to side twisting at the ankle, march in place, lift shoulders up and down, and do kicks with alternating legs.

MEANINGFUL DISCUSSION

* Did you ever play any instruments? What instrument(s) did you play? (Prompt with suggestions as needed, such as piano, guitar, violin, clarinet, trumpet, trombone, bass, flute, drums, etc.) Did you study music for a long time or only briefly?

* Have you ever been in a band? What instrument did you play in the band? (Prompt with examples as needed, see above.) What kind of band was it? (Prompt with examples as needed, such as a marching band, a jazz band, a rock band, etc.) Where did you perform?

* Where are some places you might see a marching band perform? (Prompt with examples as needed, such as a parade, high school or college football games, at patriotic or military events, etc.) Where are some places you might see a jazz band or a rock band play? (Prompt with examples as needed, such as bars, dance clubs, weddings, parties, dance halls, etc.)

* Do you have a favorite instrument? Why is it your favorite?

* Do you have a favorite band or singer? Who is it?

ALL SHOOK UP

SONG: *"All Shook Up"*
COMPOSERS/WRITERS: *Otis Blackwell & Elvis Presley (writers)*
ARTIST(S): *Elvis Presley*
YEAR(S) RELEASED: *1957*

ADDITIONAL INFORMATION

The song "All Shook Up" was written on a dare. One of Blackwell's bosses was shaking a bottle of Pepsi, and challenged Blackwell to write a song based on the phrase "all shook up." The song went on to be Elvis Presley's second-biggest hit in the United States, spending eight weeks at number one on the *Billboard* Top 100 Singles chart. "All Shook Up" was declared *Billboard*'s number one single of 1957.

ENGAGED LISTENING

Encourage your loved one to shake different parts of his or her body with the verses of the song (hands, wrists, ankles, feet, shoulders, etc.), and to sway his or her hips from side to side, "Elvis style," during the chorus.

MEANINGFUL DISCUSSION

* The singer talks about feeling shaky, weak, and tongue-tied because he is in love. Have you ever had strong feelings for someone that affected you physically? What were some of those physical feelings? (Prompt with examples as needed, such as fast heartbeat, cannot think clearly, sweating, chills, stuttering, cotton mouth, nervousness, etc.)

* Some people get nervous when they are around someone they have feelings for. Have you ever had a hard time talking to someone you had a crush on? Have you ever been approached by someone who had a crush on you? What was it like?

* Has falling in love ever shaken up your world or changed your outlook on life? How?

AMAZING GRACE

SONG: *Amazing Grace*
COMPOSERS/WRITERS: *John Newton (lyrics)*
ARTIST(S): *Various Artists*
YEAR(S) RELEASED: *1779*

ADDITIONAL INFORMATION

"Amazing Grace" was written by John Newton to describe his spiritual conversion to Christianity after his life as a slave trader. The hymn became popular in the United States during the early 19th century's Second Great Awakening, and it was paired with the tune "New Britain" in 1835 to form the song that is commonly sung today. It has been covered by many popular artists, and some of the most well-known versions include those recorded by Judy Collins, Arlo Guthrie, Joan Baez, and the instrumental version featuring bagpipes, pipes, and drums by The Royal Scots Dragoon Guards.

ENGAGED LISTENING

The first verse of this song is very well-known. Encourage your loved one to sing it along with you as you listen to this hymn together. Please note that while this song is typically sung to provide comfort, it is also commonly associated with funerals. Please be aware that some feelings that come up with this song may be focused on grief or sadness as much as salvation and comfort.

MEANINGFUL DISCUSSION

* This hymn is commonly sung to provide comfort during difficult times. Have you ever sung this hymn to get you through a hard time?

* What is this hymn about? (Prompt with examples as needed, such as redemption, salvation, comfort, God's grace, etc.) How does this hymn make you feel?

* What is grace? (being given something freely, something we do not deserve, etc.)

* Do you think God's salvation is best described as "amazing grace"? Have you experienced "amazing grace" in your own life? Can you tell me about it? How did experiencing God's love and grace change and/or define your life?

* Can you tell me what you think makes God's grace so amazing?

ANYTHING YOU CAN DO

SONG: *"Anything You Can Do"*
COMPOSERS/WRITERS: *Irving Berlin (writer)*
ARTIST(S): *Ethel Merman & Ray Middleton, Betty Hutton & Howard Keel*
YEAR(S) RELEASED: *1946 (Broadway), 1950 (film)*

ADDITIONAL INFORMATION

The song "Anything You Can Do" was written by Irving Berlin for the musical *Annie Get Your Gun*, which tells the story of Annie Oakley. During this song, Annie Oakley (played by Ethel Merman on Broadway) and Frank Butler (played by Ray Middleton on Broadway) have an argument over who is a better sharp shooter. This leads to Annie and Frank singing a duet about how each one can out-do the other.

ENGAGED LISTENING

If you have access to the Internet, search for a video clip of Betty Hutton and Howard Keel performing this song in the film to watch with your loved one.

MEANINGFUL DISCUSSION

* Have you ever had an argument or disagreement with a sibling or friend about who can do something better? If so, what was it about? Were you able to resolve your disagreement?

* In this song, the singers debate about a variety of tasks that each of them claim they can do better. Can you name some of the tasks mentioned? (be greater, sing higher, buy something cheaper, speak softer, drink liquor quicker, hold a note longer, wear something better, talk faster, sing sweeter, etc.)

* Do you think this song and the list of skills they are arguing over is serious or funny?

* What is the one thing that neither one of them can do? (bake a pie) Can you bake a pie? What kinds of pie do you like?

* Everyone has different talents and skills. What are a few things that you are really good at? What are a few things you aren't very good at?

AS TIME GOES BY

SONG: *"As Time Goes By"*
COMPOSERS/WRITERS: *Herman Hupfeld (writer)*
ARTIST(S): *Dooley Wilson*
YEAR(S) RELEASED: *Originally released in 1931; Made famous in the film* Casablanca *in 1942*

ADDITIONAL INFORMATION

In the film *Casablanca*, the song "As Time Goes By" plays throughout symbolizing the love of the two main characters, Rick (played by Humphrey Bogart) and Ilsa (played by Ingrid Bergman). "As Time Goes By" is the number two song on the American Film Institute's "100 Years...100 Songs" list of the top movie songs of all time.

ENGAGED LISTENING

While listening to this song, ask your loved one to dance, either seated or standing up. Possibly hold his or her hands to help him or her move along with this song.

MEANINGFUL DISCUSSION

* The song talks about the enduring nature of love. Do you think the fundamentals of love stay the same from generation to generation, "as time goes by"? Do you think love stories will also endure, even "as time goes by" like the song suggests?

* The song states that signs of affection, such as saying, "I love you," also remain constant "as time goes by" and from generation to generation. Do you think that is true? What is a special way you and your sweetheart demonstrate(d) affection?

* Did you ever see the film *Casablanca*? Do you remember any of these famous lines from the film? Encourage your loved one to complete each quote you start, if he or she is able. Prompt with the following suggested quotes: "Here's looking at you, kid." "Sing it, Sam." (Apparently, nobody said "Play it again Sam" in the film but there are some who recall it differently!) "We'll always have Paris." "Of all the gin joints in all the towns in all the world, she walks into mine."

BEER BARREL POLKA

SONG: *"Beer Barrel Polka"*
COMPOSERS/WRITERS: *Jaromir Vejvoda (music), Lew Brown & Wladimir Timm (lyrics)*
ARTIST(S): *Will Glahe (instrumental), Frank Yankovic & His Yanks*
YEAR(S) RELEASED: *1927 (published), 1939 (released)*

ADDITIONAL INFORMATION

"Beer Barrel Polka," also known as "Roll Out the Barrel" and "The Barrel Polka," was originally a Czechoslovakian song, composed by Jaromir Vejvoda in 1927. Lew Brown and Wladimir Timm wrote the lyrics and when it was first released in 1939 by Will Glahe it was number one on *Your Hit Parade*. "Beer Barrel Polka" became popular around the world during World War II and was said to have been enjoyed by soldiers on both sides. Since then it has been recorded by multiple artists.

ENGAGED LISTENING

Encourage your loved one to move along with this upbeat polka. Suggested movements include: clap hands, tap toes, march in place, kicks, and swing arms.

MEANINGFUL DISCUSSION

* Have you ever danced the polka? Who taught you? Where did you go to dance the polka?

* When dancing the polka, do you like to stay with the same partner or switch to different partners?

* This song talks about how people feel better when they hear the polka and dance. Do you feel better when you hear music? What kinds of music make you feel happy? (Prompt with examples as needed, such as rock and roll, jazz, country, pop, hymns, big band, classical, Broadway, gospel, etc.) Do you feel better when you dance?

* Do you like to drink beer? What kind of beer do you like? What other beverages do you think of when you think of celebrating? (Prompt with examples as needed, such as champagne, wine, punch, lemonade, egg nog, etc.)

BILL BAILEY, WON'T YOU PLEASE COME HOME

SONG: *"Bill Bailey, Won't You Please Come Home"*
COMPOSERS/WRITERS: *Hughie Cannon (writer)*
ARTIST(S): *Jimmy Durante, Patsy Cline*
YEAR(S) RELEASED: *1902*

ADDITIONAL INFORMATION

"Bill Bailey, Won't You Please Come Home," also known as "Bill Bailey" and "Won't You Come Home, Bill Bailey," is considered by some to be the most popular ragtime tune ever written, and is still a jazz standard today. According to several sources, the popular song tells the true, sad story of a country girl who disregarded her mother's advice to avoid "city boys" and was left with a husband who was out at odd hours in Jackson, Michigan. The chorus of this song is most familiar and is commonly sung on its own.

ENGAGED LISTENING

Encourage your loved one to move along with you as you listen together.
Suggested movements include: tap toes, kicks, and shake and shrug shoulders.

MEANINGFUL DISCUSSION

* Who do you think is waiting for Bill Bailey to come home? (his wife)

* The chorus of this song suggests that a fight or disagreement is the reason Bill Bailey is not at home. Did you ever storm off in the middle of an argument? Do you think this is a good response to a disagreement?

* What are some other ways you can handle a disagreement in the heat of the moment?

* Have you ever had a really big fight with someone you cared about? How did the two of you resolve it?

* Everyone has different ways of cooling off after a disagreement. How do you calm down after having a fight with someone you love? What are some of the most effective ways for you personally to resolve a disagreement?

BLUE SKIES

SONG: *"Blue Skies"*
COMPOSERS/WRITERS: *Irving Berlin (writer)*
ARTIST(S): *Belle Baker, Ben Selvin, Al Jolson*
YEAR(S) RELEASED: *1926/1927*

ADDITIONAL INFORMATION

"Blue Skies" was a last-minute addition to *Betsy*, a 1926 musical by Rodgers and Hart. The sheet music was published the following year, and the song was a number one hit. Al Jolson performed it in 1927 in *The Jazz Singer*, making it one of the first songs to be featured in a talkie, or movie with sound and dialogue. The song has been covered by numerous artists, including Bing Crosby, Ella Fitzgerald, Count Basie, Bennie Goodman, and Willie Nelson.

ENGAGED LISTENING

Encourage your loved one to tap his or her toes and snap his or her fingers along with this song. Remember, your loved one will be more likely to move if he or she sees you moving as well. If finger snaps are challenging, encourage your loved one to clap instead. If you have a window nearby, take a look out the window to see what kind of day it is and compare to the lyrics in the song (blue skies, plenty of sunshine, or a cloudy day).

MEANINGFUL DISCUSSION

* What is it that makes the singer notice the days hurrying by? (He or she is in love.) What did it feel like when you fell in love? Did you feel like everything was brighter, happier, and generally better?

* Have you ever had a day where it felt like everything was going right? What made it feel that way? Do you think it was luck, having the right attitude, love, motivation, hard work, or something else?

* Have you ever accomplished something that made you feel like the rest of the day would be good no matter what happened? What was it? (Prompt with examples as needed, such as got a job, got a promotion, passed a hard test, heard good news from family or friends, heard your favorite song on the radio, bought a house, bought a new car, etc.)

BRIDGE OVER TROUBLED WATER

SONG: *"Bridge over Troubled Water"*
COMPOSERS/WRITERS: *Paul Simon (writer)*
ARTIST(S): *Simon & Garfunkel*
YEAR(S) RELEASED: *1970*

ADDITIONAL INFORMATION

This song was one of the first songs longer than three minutes to play on pop radio. It maintained the number one spot on both the *Billboard* Hot 100 and Adult Contemporary charts for six weeks. It is ranked as *Billboard*'s number one song for the year 1970 and is one of few songs to top charts in both the United States and the United Kingdom simultaneously. "Bridge over Troubled Water" has been covered by over 50 different artists, including Elvis Presley, Aretha Franklin, Johnny Cash, and Willie Nelson.

ENGAGED LISTENING

While listening to this song, hold your loved one's hands and sway gently side to side with the music.

MEANINGFUL DISCUSSION

- What is this song about? What does the song mean by "bridge over troubled water"? (This song is a promise of enduring support from a friend, who promises to be like a "bridge" or a help through a difficult time.)
- Is there someone in your life who is your "bridge over troubled water"? Who has always been there for you? What does he or she say or do to support you?
- This song is about comfort and friendship. Who is your best friend? How long have you known him or her? When and where did you meet? Are you still in contact today? What are some qualities that make him or her your best friend?
- Do you remember a time when you helped someone else through a difficult situation? What happened?

BUTTON UP YOUR OVERCOAT

SONG: *"Button Up Your Overcoat"*
COMPOSERS/WRITERS: *Ray Henderson (music), B.G. DeSylva & Lew Brown (lyrics)*
ARTIST(S): *Ruth Etting, Helen Kane*
YEAR(S) RELEASED: *1928/1929*

ADDITIONAL INFORMATION

The song "Button Up Your Overcoat" was written in 1928 for the Broadway musical *Follow Thru*, which premiered in 1929. Ruth Etting was one of the first artists to record the song and other notable recordings include Helen Kane (the voice of Betty Boop), Bing Crosby, and Nat King Cole.

ENGAGED LISTENING

While listening to this song, encourage your loved one to wave hands with open palms to the beat and tap toes side to side, twisting at the ankle. Also encourage your loved one to sing with you and emphasize the "ooo-ooo"s throughout the song.

MEANINGFUL DISCUSSION

* This song describes how to take care of yourself. Can you name some ideas mentioned in the song? (Prompt with examples as needed, such as buttoning your coat, eating an apple daily, avoiding meat and sweets, wearing flannel underwear, etc.)

* Why should you button up your overcoat on a windy day?

* Do you think it is good advice to "eat an apple every day"?

* Would you follow the advice to "get to bed by three"? Do you think the singer is referring to 3PM or 3AM?

* What are some things you can do to take good care of yourself? (Prompt with examples as needed, such as exercising, eating healthy foods, drinking water, engaging in activities you enjoy, resting, etc.)

BYE BYE BLACKBIRD

SONG: *"Bye Bye Blackbird"*
COMPOSERS/WRITERS: *Ray Henderson (music), Mort Dixon (lyrics)*
ARTIST(S): *Sam Lanin & His Dance Orchestra, Nick Lucas, Gene Austin*
YEAR(S) RELEASED: *1926*

ADDITIONAL INFORMATION

"Bye Bye Blackbird" was first recorded by Sam Lanin's Dance Orchestra in 1926, and it was made popular by both Gene Austin and Nick Lucas in that same year. This song continued to stay popular through the Great Depression and has appeared in numerous films by various artists. There is some controversy over the meaning of the lyrics, however, most agree that the "blackbird" represents a dark or challenging time that the singer has now overcome. Some notable versions include those by Eddie Cantor, Miles Davis, Peggy Lee, John Coltrane, Julie London, Dean Martin, and Joe Cocker.

ENGAGED LISTENING

While listening to this song, hold hands with your loved one and sway from
side to side or stand up and dance together if your loved one is able.

MEANINGFUL DISCUSSION

* How would you feel if you could "pack up all your cares and woes" like the singer mentions in the song? Would it feel like a weight has been lifted or that you were just ignoring problems? Is it easy to just pack up your problems?

* Some say that the "blackbird" represents a challenging time that the singer has overcome. Has there been a challenging time in your life that you were able to get through? Did you have help or support? If so, from who? Have you been there to help someone else out of a challenging situation? What did you do to help and support him or her?

* In the song, the singer says to make his bed and leave the light on as he will be arriving late. Have you ever come back late from a long trip or journey to find that someone you care about left the light on for you? Did it feel good to know that someone you cared about was waiting for you? What are other ways you can welcome a loved one home?

* Is the singer happy to be returning to home from a difficult situation? What makes coming home so comforting? When you think of home, is it a place, a person, or a state of mind?

CHATTANOOGA CHOO CHOO

SONG: *"Chattanooga Choo Choo"*
COMPOSERS/WRITERS: *Mack Gordon (lyrics), Harry Warren (music)*
ARTIST(S): *The Glenn Miller Orchestra*
YEAR(S) RELEASED: *1941*

ADDITIONAL INFORMATION

It is said that the inspiration for this song was a locomotive that traveled from Cincinnati, Ohio to Chattanooga, Tennessee. The song "Chattanooga Choo Choo" first debuted in the film *Sun Valley Serenade*, in 1941. This song became the number one song in the United States in December, 1941, and stayed at the top for nine weeks. The Andrews Sisters also recorded a popular version and the song has since been covered by numerous artists.

ENGAGED LISTENING

While listening to this song, encourage your loved one to tap his or her toes and sway from side to side. If your loved one is able and interested, encourage him or her to get up and dance. If you are both seated, hold hands and sway side to side and forwards and backwards.

MEANINGFUL DISCUSSION

* Have you ever been on a train? Where have you traveled to by train? Was it a short or long trip?

* Do you enjoy traveling by train? What do you like about it?

* What are some advantages of train travel? (Prompt with examples as needed, such as it's a great way to see the scenery of different states/countries, you don't have to stop as you can eat and sleep on the train, trains originally enabled people to travel longer distances than they could before, etc.)

* What kinds of different cars are on a train? (Prompt with examples as needed, such as baggage cars, dining car, cafe car, observation car, passenger car, sleeping car, etc.)

DAISY BELL (BICYCLE BUILT FOR TWO)

SONG: *Daisy Bell (Bicycle Built for Two)*
COMPOSERS/WRITERS: *Harry Dacre (writer)*
ARTIST(S): *Dinah Shore, Nat King Cole*
YEAR(S) RELEASED: *1892*

ADDITIONAL INFORMATION

When Harry Dacre moved to the United States, he was apparently charged an import duty for his bicycle. A friend joked, "It's lucky you didn't bring a bicycle built for two, otherwise you'd have to pay double duty." Harry Dacre found this amusing and it helped inspire this song.

ENGAGED LISTENING

Encourage your loved one to sway side to side with the rhythm of this song as you listen together. If you are able to connect to the Internet, find a picture of a tandem bicycle to assist with the discussion below.

MEANINGFUL DISCUSSION

* Have you ever ridden on a bicycle built for two? If so, did you sit up front or in the back? If you are sitting in the front you are the one with the control over where you both go. How did you feel about being in control of where you both go or being unable to control where the bicycle goes?

* Did you enjoy riding a bicycle? Did you own a bicycle? If so, what color was your bicycle? Did you ride it to school or to a friend's house? Where else did you ride your bicycle?

* Would you ride away on a bicycle on your wedding day as mentioned in the lyrics? Why or why not?

* If you were Daisy, would you accept the proposal under the terms in the song? Would you marry someone who could not afford a carriage for your wedding day? Why or why not?

DANNY BOY

SONG: *"Danny Boy"*
COMPOSERS/WRITERS: *Frederic Weatherly (lyrics)*
ARTIST(S): *The Irish Tenors, Bing Crosby, Eva Cassidy*
YEAR(S) RELEASED: *1913 (published), 1915 (recorded)*

ADDITIONAL INFORMATION

The song "Danny Boy" was originally written to a different melody, then re-set to "Londonderry Air," a traditional Irish tune from the mid-19th century. Frederic Weatherly, who wrote the lyrics, was an English lawyer believed to have never set foot in Ireland. The song is typically sung with four verses in the United States and six in Ireland. It is commonly interpreted to be a song about a boy going to war. Some notable recordings include Glenn Miller, Conway Twitty, Judy Garland, Johnny Cash, Elvis Presley, and Harry Connick Jr.

ENGAGED LISTENING

If you have access to the Internet, search for pictures of the Irish countryside and/or some of the Irish landmarks listed in the questions below to aid in the discussion. It is important to note that this song can evoke feelings of both happiness and sadness. If your loved one becomes tearful during this song, ask if he or she would like to still listen to the song and if the tears are happy or sad tears. This information will help aid in the discussion below and also indicate if you should continue.

MEANINGFUL DISCUSSION

* What is this song about? (A boy is going away, and the singer is waiting for his return. It is also about the enduring nature of love, despite distances and challenges.)

* The singer declares she will still be waiting for her sweetheart's return, no matter what. Do you think true love endures despite any circumstances? Is there sadness in the lyrics as the singer ponders how long she might wait for her true love's return?

* Did you ever have a true love? Were there ever any circumstances that made your relationship challenging? How did your love endure despite those challenges?

* This song is set in Ireland. Have you ever been to Ireland? What do you remember about it?

* What are some things Ireland is famous for? (Prompt with examples as needed, such as shamrocks, Guinness beer, rolling green countryside, potatoes, the Cliffs of Moher, the Ring of Kerry, the Blarney Stone, Irish dancing, etc.)

DON'T SIT UNDER THE APPLE TREE
(WITH ANYONE ELSE BUT ME)

SONG: *"Don't Sit Under the Apple Tree (with Anyone Else but Me)"*
COMPOSERS/WRITERS: *Lew Brown & Charles Tobias (lyrics), Sam H. Stept (music)*
ARTIST(S): *The Glenn Miller Orchestra, The Andrews Sisters*
YEAR(S) RELEASED: *1939 (Broadway version), 1942 (The Glenn Miller Orchestra, The Andrews Sisters)*

ADDITIONAL INFORMATION

The song "Don't Sit Under the Apple Tree" was originally written for *Yokel Boy*, a 1939 Broadway musical. The lyrics were modified to the version that is now most well-known, including the chorus "when I come marching home," after the United States entered World War II in 1941. It held the number one spot on the television and radio show *Your Hit Parade* longer than any other wartime song.

ENGAGED LISTENING

Encourage your loved one to shake his or her head or wag his or her finger during the "No! No! No!" part of the song. If singing along, encourage your loved one to sing that part emphatically as well. March in place as you listen and prompt your loved one to do the same.

MEANINGFUL DISCUSSION

* What is this song about? (A soldier asking his sweetheart to be true to him while he is off at war.) Have you ever asked a loved one to wait for you? Have you ever waited for someone else? What were some ways you kept in touch with your loved one from a distance?

* In this song, two places that are special to the sweethearts are mentioned; what are they? (under the apple tree, lover's lane) Do (did) you and your sweetheart share any places that were special to just the two of you? What are (were) they?

* What happened during the early 1940s that made this song so relevant? (After the United States entered World War II, many young men joined the military and were sent overseas to fight, leaving their girlfriends, wives, and sweethearts behind.)

* Have you ever gone apple picking? What are some things you can make with apples? (Prompt with examples as needed, such as applesauce, apple pie, apple cider, apple dumplings, apple crisp, fried apples, etc.)

DOWNTOWN

SONG: *"Downtown"*
COMPOSERS/WRITERS: *Tony Hatch (writer)*
ARTIST(S): *Petula Clark*
YEAR(S) RELEASED: *1964*

ADDITIONAL INFORMATION

Petula Clark was a star in the United Kingdom whose music was already catching on in France as well, before she became popular in America with the hit "Downtown" in 1964. The song was number one on the *Billboard* Hot 100 chart in the United States and went on to win the Grammy for "Best Rock and Roll Recording" in 1965.

ENGAGED LISTENING

Encourage your loved one to sway side to side with you as you listen to the song together. If you have access to the Internet, find pictures of the downtowns of major cities in America. Try to choose a city or cities that may be familiar to your loved one based on where he or she lived or a favorite city he or she visited frequently.

MEANINGFUL DISCUSSION

* Where does the song suggest you can go when you are having a bad day? (downtown)

* What are some of the things you might see or do downtown as suggested in the song? (traffic, neon signs, bright lights, movie shows, dancing, places that never close, etc.)

* Have you ever been downtown before? In what city? What were some of the things you saw there? What are some of the things you enjoyed doing downtown?

* What are some of the differences between living in a big city and a small town? If you live(d) in a small town, did it also have a downtown?

* When you think of going downtown, what is the first city that comes to mind? Have you ever been there? What made visiting that city so memorable? (This answer may be the same or very similar to the above question. Perhaps use this time to prompt your loved one for more details.)

* The song suggests the distractions of being downtown are a great way to forget problems, worries, and loneliness; do you agree or disagree? Sometimes when things trouble us, we do need a distraction, however, other times ignoring a problem will not make it go away.

* What are some things you do when you are having worries or feeling lonely? (Prompt with suggestions as needed, such as call or talk to a friend or family member, ask for help, seek out a fun distraction, take a walk, take a few deep breaths, etc.)

EDELWEISS

SONG: *"Edelweiss"*
COMPOSERS/WRITERS: *Oscar Hammerstein II (lyrics), Richard Rodgers (music)*
ARTIST(S): *Theodore Bikel, Bill Lee & Charmain Carr*
YEAR(S) RELEASED: *1959 (Broadway musical), 1965 (film)*

ADDITIONAL INFORMATION

This song was made popular in the 1959 Broadway musical *The Sound of Music*, and was adapted for film in 1965. Mary Martin played the role of Maria on Broadway, however, most people remember Julie Andrews in the film version. Edelweiss is a white flower found high in the Alps. Though it is illegal to pick, it is considered to bring good luck to anybody who sees one. A common misconception is that the song is the national anthem for Austria, but in fact it was written for the musical.

ENGAGED LISTENING

Try holding your loved one's hands and gently sway side to side with the rhythm for the first half of the song, and gently swing his or her arms up and down for the second half. If you have access to the Internet, look up pictures of the edelweiss flower. It is a unique flower and the images will help foster the discussion below.

MEANINGFUL DISCUSSION

* What is an edelweiss? Have you ever seen one? (If not, refer to a picture.) How is this flower different from the flowers we see around us?

* What is your favorite flower? (Prompt with examples of different types of flowers as needed, such as roses, daisies, lilies, chrysanthemums, tulips, carnations, violets, etc.)

* What are some reasons to send someone flowers? (Prompt with examples as needed, such as birthday, anniversary, Valentine's Day, new baby, etc.)

* It is said that this flower brings good luck. What other things are thought to bring good luck? (Prompt with examples as needed, such as rabbit's foot, four-leaf clover, horseshoe, lucky penny, good luck pig, etc.)

* How does the song describe the edelweiss flower? (small, white, clean, bright, greeting the singer in the morning, etc.) Do you think the singer sees the flower as a sign of hope? What are some other signs you consider to be signs of hope? (Prompt with examples as needed, such as a rainbow, sunshine, something personal to your loved one, etc.)

GEORGIA ON MY MIND

SONG: *"Georgia on My Mind"*
COMPOSERS/WRITERS: *Hoagy Carmichael (music), Stuart Gorrell (lyrics)*
ARTIST(S): *Ray Charles*
YEAR(S) RELEASED: *1930 (Hoagy Carmichael), 1960 (Ray Charles)*

ADDITIONAL INFORMATION

Though it is often speculated that this song was written about Hoagy Carmichael's sister Georgia, Carmichael himself has stated that he wrote it about the state of Georgia. "Georgia on My Mind" has been recorded by many famous artists including Dean Martin, Glenn Miller, Willie Nelson, Louis Armstrong, and, most famously, Ray Charles. The Ray Charles version reached number one on the United States *Billboard* Hot 100 chart in 1960, and the following year the song was officially adopted as the state song of Georgia.

ENGAGED LISTENING

As you sit and listen to this song with your loved one, encourage him or her
to take relaxing breaths in and out.

MEANINGFUL DISCUSSION

* This is the state song of Georgia. Have you ever been to Georgia? If so, what do you remember about it? What are some things Georgia is known for? (Prompt with examples as needed, such as peaches, Vidalia onions, football, pine trees, pecans, peanuts, the Masters golf tournament, Coca-Cola, etc.)

* The singer talks about how other places are appealing, but "the road leads back" to Georgia. Have you ever gone away from home for a while and then returned? How did it feel? What did you miss the most when you were gone?

* If you have ever been away from your home, is there anything that reminds you of home? (sights, smells, sounds, etc.) Does it comfort you to think of these things? What are some of the things your home state is known for?

* Do you think home brings a sense of peace that you can't find anywhere else, like the song suggests?

GETTING TO KNOW YOU

SONG: *"Getting to Know You"*
COMPOSERS/WRITERS: *Oscar Hammerstein II (lyrics), Richard Rodgers (music)*
ARTIST(S): *Gertrude Lawrence, Marni Nixon*
YEAR(S) RELEASED: *1951 (Broadway), 1956 (film)*

ADDITIONAL INFORMATION

"Getting to Know You" is a Broadway hit from the 1951 musical *The King and I*, by Rodgers and Hammerstein. Gertrude Lawrence sang it in the original Broadway production, while Marni Nixon recorded it for the 1956 movie adaptation in which the role of Anna was played by Deborah Kerr.

ENGAGED LISTENING

Sway side to side with your loved one as you listen to this song together.

MEANINGFUL DISCUSSION

* How do you get to know someone? (Prompt with examples as needed, such as say hello, introduce yourself, ask about his or her interests, spend time together, listen to one another, etc.)

* Tell me how you met and got to know your best friend!

* What are some ways to meet new friends?

* Did you ever meet a friend in a really unusual way?

* If your loved one is in a retirement community, ask the following question: What are some ways you can meet new friends here at this community? (Prompt with examples as needed, such as attend activities and programs offered, sit with someone new at lunch or dinner, smile, encourage other residents to attend one of the activities with you, introduce yourself and strike up a conversation, etc.)

* What is something interesting about you, to help me get to know you better? (You can also share something interesting about yourself that your loved one may not know.)

(GHOST) RIDERS IN THE SKY: A COWBOY LEGEND

SONG: *"(Ghost) Riders in the Sky: A Cowboy Legend"*
COMPOSERS/WRITERS: *Stan Jones (writer)*
ARTIST(S): *Vaughn Monroe*
YEAR(S) RELEASED: *1949*

ADDITIONAL INFORMATION

"(Ghost) Riders in the Sky," also known as "A Cowboy Legend," was ranked by *Billboard* as the number one song for 1949. Written by Stan Jones, the melody is based on the song "When Johnny Comes Marching Home" and it is said to be the most recorded Western song of all time. It was first recorded by Burl Ives, but Vaughn Monroe's version, released a month later, is the most famous. This song has been recorded by countless artists over several decades.

ENGAGED LISTENING

Encourage your loved one to move along with you to this energetic song. Prompt him or her to complete some of the following movements: tap toes, tap heels, march in place, pat the beat on his or her knees, clap hands, and then try a combination of these movements (i.e., clap and march). Consider encouraging your loved one to swing his or her arms overhead, imitating throwing a lasso, moving one arm at a time.

MEANINGFUL DISCUSSION

* How would you describe the mood of this song? (Prompt with suggestions as needed, such as dark, mysterious, haunting, scary, energetic, eerie, etc.)

* What is this song about? (A cowboy has a vision of cowboy hell. He sees the ghosts of departed cowboys chasing "the Devil's herd" of cattle across the sky, a chase that will go on for eternity. He is warned to change his ways in order to avoid their fate.)

* Was there ever a time in your life a person or an event prompted you to change your ways? How did you change and are you glad you did?

* What sort of things or images come to mind when you think about cowboys driving cattle? (Prompt with suggestions as needed, such as cowboys on horses, lassos, large herds of cows, cowboy hats, dusty trails, long hot days, cowboy boots, etc.)

* This is considered one of the most popular and frequently recorded Western songs of all time. Have you ever traveled out West? Where did you go? What do you remember about your time there?

GOD BLESS AMERICA

SONG: *"God Bless America"*
COMPOSERS/WRITERS: *Irving Berlin (writer)*
ARTIST(S): *Kate Smith*
YEAR(S) RELEASED: *1918 (published), 1938 (debuted)*

ADDITIONAL INFORMATION

Irving Berlin originally wrote "God Bless America" in 1918, while serving in the United States Army. It was intended for a musical revue entitled *Yip Yip Yaphank*, which was to be performed where Berlin was stationed at Camp Upton. Ultimately, he decided to cut the song and filed it away. As tensions mounted worldwide in 1938, Irving Berlin revisited his song "God Bless America." After making slight changes to the lyrics and melody, his final version, the one we know today, was debuted by Kate Smith on her annual Armistice Day radio broadcast in 1938. After the song debuted, Irving Berlin did not feel comfortable accepting royalties from it and instead created the "God Bless America Fund" to help The Boy Scouts and Girl Scouts of America.

ENGAGED LISTENING

During the introduction, encourage your loved one to put his or her hand over their heart. When the melody for "God Bless America" starts, encourage your loved one to slowly march in place with the beat of the song and sing along.

MEANINGFUL DISCUSSION

* When you hear this song, how does it make you feel?

* Do you think this song brings people together? If so, how? (If your loved one is struggling, suggest some ideas such as a shared sense of patriotism, unity, working towards a common goal—the good of our nation, etc.)

* Do you remember Kate Smith singing this song on the radio or on television?

* During World War II, when this song was written, and in several subsequent wars, many Americans served their country both overseas and at home. Did you help with a war effort? If so, during which war and how did you help serve our country?

* The author of the song served in the United States Army. Have you ever served in the military? What branch? Do you have any loved ones who have served in the military?

HAPPY TRAILS

SONG: *"Happy Trails"*
COMPOSERS/WRITERS: *Credit is given to Dale Evans, see additional information*
ARTIST(S): *Roy Rodgers*
YEAR(S) RELEASED: *1952*

ADDITIONAL INFORMATION

In 1952, the husband and wife Western duo Roy Rogers and Dale Evans began to end their television program, *The Roy Rogers Show*, with the song "Happy Trails." There is still some controversy over who originally wrote the song. Dale Evans is credited as the writer, however, in 1951, Foy Willing of "Riders of the Purple Sage" wrote a song titled "Happy Trails in Sunshine Valley." Willing's group used to sing vocals with Roy Rogers and Dale Evans on their radio and television shows as well as in their films. It is said that Evans changed the lyrics and title and started using it as *The Roy Rogers Show* theme song a year later in 1952. The song "Happy Trails" is included on the "Top 100 Western Songs of All Time" list as compiled by the Western Writers of America in 2010.

ENGAGED LISTENING

Shrug your shoulders and tap your toes, encouraging your loved one to do the same.

MEANINGFUL DISCUSSION

* Did you ever listen to *The Roy Rogers Show* on the radio or watch it on television? If so, was it a family activity?

* Do you remember the name of their horse (Trigger) or their dog (Bullet)?

* What does it feel like when you spend time with someone you care about or haven't seen in a while? Do you have the feeling that seeing him or her "brings the sunny weather"?

* What does it mean to wish someone "happy trails"? (You are wishing them all the best, wherever they may go.)

* "Happy trails" is a unique way to say goodbye. What are some other ways to say goodbye to a dear friend? (Prompt with examples as needed, such as "see you later alligator, after a while crocodile", "see you in the funny papers" ,"until next time, take care", "toodle-oo", "so long", "farewell", "adieu", "ciao", "adios", etc.)

HAS ANYBODY SEEN MY GAL?
(FIVE FOOT TWO, EYES OF BLUE)

SONG: *"Has Anybody Seen My Gal? (Five Foot Two, Eyes of Blue)"*
COMPOSERS/WRITERS: *Sam M. Lewis & Joseph Widow Young (lyrics), Ray Henderson (music)*
ARTIST(S): *California Ramblers*
YEAR(S) RELEASED: *1925*

ADDITIONAL INFORMATION

While Lewis, Young, and Henderson are generally credited as the writers of this song, there are conflicting sources as to who was the original writer, especially as there were several early versions with adjusted lyrics and added or removed verses. Some sources credit Percy Wenrich and Jack Mahoney as composing the song in 1914. Regardless, the song remained quite popular throughout the 1920s and has been recorded by numerous artists. While it was officially titled "Has Anybody Seen My Gal?" it is better known as "Five Foot Two, Eyes of Blue."

ENGAGED LISTENING

Encourage your loved one to dance along with you as you listen to this song together. Suggested movements include tapping toes, heel lifts, kicks, waving hands with open palms to the beat, swaying side to side, and shaking and moving shoulders.

MEANINGFUL DISCUSSION

* How does the singer describe his gal? (relatively short, blue eyes, turned-up nose, never had another sweetheart, wears no diamonds or furs, flapper, etc. Please note that there are some variations in the lyrics.)

* Is the singer fond of his girl? (Very much so!) Do (did) you have a sweetheart you are very fond of? How would you describe him or her? What was something that immediately caught your eye when you saw your sweetheart for the first time?

* The singer praises his gal for being so loving, despite having no fancy accessories and being short in stature. Are there any attributes you think are more important in a partner than looks or fancy clothes? If so, what are they? (Prompt with suggestions as needed, such as sense of humor, caring, outgoing, creative, smart, kind, generous, loving, etc.)

HELLO DOLLY!

SONG: *"Hello Dolly!"*
COMPOSERS/WRITERS: *Jerry Herman (writer)*
ARTIST(S): *Louis Armstrong, Carol Channing, Barbra Streisand*
YEAR(S) RELEASED: *1964*

ADDITIONAL INFORMATION

"Hello Dolly!" is the title song for the Broadway musical of the same name, which premiered in 1964 and starred Carol Channing as Dolly Gallagher Levi. The film version came out in 1969 starring Barbra Streisand. Louis Armstrong's 1964 version of the song became a number one hit in the United States and won a Grammy award for "Best Vocal Performance." When the recording was first released, Louis Armstrong was the oldest artist to top the United States charts, at age 62. The musical *Hello Dolly!* was based on Thornton Wilder's 1938 play *The Merchant of Yonkers*, which he revised and renamed *The Matchmaker* in 1955. The musical follows the day-to-day life of Dolly, who works as a matchmaker. As she is trying to set up Horace Vandergelder, she decides that she will be the one to marry him. The Broadway musical *Hello Dolly!* won a record-breaking ten Tony awards.

ENGAGED LISTENING

Encourage your loved one to sway side to side and move his or her shoulders along with this lively song. Encourage him or her to kick as if in a chorus line as well.

MEANINGFUL DISCUSSION

* Have you ever seen *Hello Dolly!*? Did you enjoy it? Did you see a film version or did you see it live?

* Have you ever tried to play matchmaker like the character Dolly does in the show? If so, how did it go? If not, do you think you would be good at it? At one point in the show Dolly describes her job as "meddling." Would you agree with that?

* Did anyone ever try to play matchmaker and set you up with someone? How did it work out?

* Did you participate in theatre in school? If so, what productions were you in? Were you on stage or did you help behind the scenes?

HERE COMES THE SUN

SONG: *"Here Comes the Sun"*
COMPOSERS/WRITERS: *George Harrison (writer)*
ARTIST(S): *The Beatles*
YEAR(S) RELEASED: *1969*

ADDITIONAL INFORMATION

This song was written by George Harrison and appeared on the Beatles' 1969 album *Abbey Road*. Harrison wrote the song to express his relief at the arrival of spring. The song was recorded by three of the four Beatles: George Harrison, Paul McCartney, and Ringo Starr. John Lennon was not involved in the process because he was recovering from a car crash at the time.

ENGAGED LISTENING

If possible, look out the window with your loved one while listening to this song and observe your surroundings. Point out anything interesting (the sun, the clouds, the color of the sky, any flowers or trees you see, people moving about, etc.)

MEANINGFUL DISCUSSION

* How does seeing the sun shining outside make you feel? What are some things you enjoy doing when the sun is shining? (Prompt with suggestions as needed, such as sit outside, take a walk, garden, run errands, etc.)

* How does it make you feel to see the sunshine after several cloudy or rainy days in a row? Does it make you feel more energized or happy? Does it make you feel better to see the sun like they say in the song?

* This song talks about the transition from a "long, cold, lonely winter" into springtime. Do you prefer the winter or the spring? Why? Do you have a favorite season? If so, which one and why?

* What are some things you associate with springtime? (Prompt with examples as needed, such as flowers in bloom, birds chirping, warmer weather, longer days, more sunshine, biking, going for walks, having a picnic, going for a jog, golfing, gardening, baseball, flying a kite, seeing more animals and people out and about, etc.)

* What season is it now? What are some things outside that indicate what time of year it is?

HEY, GOOD LOOKIN'

SONG: *"Hey, Good Lookin'"*
COMPOSERS/WRITERS: *Cole Porter (writer), Hank Williams (writer)*
ARTIST(S): *Hank Williams*
YEAR(S) RELEASED: *1951*

ADDITIONAL INFORMATION

This song, written by Hank Williams, was based on a 1942 Cole Porter song with the same title. Hank Williams originally wrote this song for his friend and fellow musician, Jimmy Dickens, but then recorded it himself instead, telling Dickens, "That song's too good for you!" This song has been covered by several different artists, including Jo Stafford and Frankie Laine, Johnny Cash, Dean Martin, and Jimmy Buffett.

ENGAGED LISTENING

Encourage your loved one to tap his or her toes and/or move his or her shoulders along with you as you listen to this song together. If you have access to the Internet, search for a video clip of Hank Williams performing this song live. He gives an energetic performance and is always dressed in his very finest!

MEANINGFUL DISCUSSION

* What is this song about? (The singer is trying to convince the listener to go on a date with him.) Have you ever asked someone out on a date?

* Have you ever had to convince someone to give you a chance and go on a date with you? Did he (she) eventually say yes? What did you do or say to persuade him (her) to give you a chance? How did the date go?

* Has anyone ever had to work to convince you to give him (her) a chance to go on a date with him (her)? What made you eventually say yes? How did the date go?

* "Hey, good lookin'" can be considered a pickup line. What are some other pickup lines you've heard or used in the past?

* The song talks about buying a book for "five or ten cents." What else could you buy for five or ten cents when you were growing up? (Prompt with examples as needed, such as candy, gum, a newspaper, a phone call, mailing a letter, etc.) What can you buy for that price now?

HOME ON THE RANGE

SONG: *"Home on the Range"*
COMPOSERS/WRITERS: *Traditional Folk Song (authorship believed to be Higley & Kelly)*
ARTIST(S): *Gene Autry, Roy Rogers*
YEAR(S) RELEASED: *1867*

ADDITIONAL INFORMATION

"Home on the Range" has a complicated history, which includes strong associations with a variety of locations, multiple early versions of the song, and competing claims of authorship. It is believed the song became widespread as cowboys sang it while they drove cattle along the Chisholm Trail. Franklin D. Roosevelt declared it to be his favorite song, which served to increase its popularity. "Home on the Range" became the state song of Kansas in 1947. Over the years, this song has become timeless with many famous artists recording their own version, including Bing Crosby, Frank Sinatra, and Bugs Bunny. It is interesting to note that even though there are many versions of this song, it never made it to the top of the charts.

ENGAGED LISTENING

The chorus of this song is very well-known. Sing along as you listen and encourage your loved one to do the same.

MEANINGFUL DISCUSSION

- What does the author of this song say about his home? How does he describe his "home on the range"? (the skies are never cloudy, the breezes are balmy and light, the air is pure, one seldom hears a discouraging word, the deer and the antelope are at play, the buffalo roam, there is bright diamond sand, etc.)

- Does the author like his home?

- Folk songs celebrate our shared home here in America. What are some great things about calling America "home"?

- What makes a place a "home"?

- Describe your home. (Your loved one could describe his or her childhood home, maybe the home where he or she raised a family, his or her current home, etc.)

- What made (makes) your home special?

- If your loved one is in a retirement community, ask the following questions: What about your home now? What are some things that make this community special? (Prompt with examples as needed, such as friends, fun activities, good meals, own room with own decorations, do not have to cook or clean, able to go on outings, etc.)

HOUND DOG

SONG: *"Hound Dog"*
COMPOSERS/WRITERS: *Jerry Lieber & Mike Stoller (writers), Johnny Otis (producer)*
ARTIST(S): *Elvis Presley*
YEAR(S) RELEASED: *1956*

ADDITIONAL INFORMATION

The Elvis Presley version of "Hound Dog" was released as a single on the flip side of "Don't Be Cruel," and was the only single to have both sides reach number one in the United States. The song topped the *Billboard* Pop, Country, and R&B charts simultaneously in 1956, and held the number one spot on the Pop chart for 11 weeks. The song has been recorded over 250 times. Presley's 1956 version is ranked number 19 on *Rolling Stone*'s "500 Greatest Songs of All Time" list. While the song was made famous by Elvis Presley, it was first released in 1953 by Willie Mae "Big Mama" Thornton.

ENGAGED LISTENING

While listening to the song, encourage your loved one to stand (if able) and sway his or her hips from side to side. You can also clap along to the rhythm of the song and dance in your chair while encouraging your loved one to do the same. If you have access to the Internet, search for a video clip of Elvis performing "Hound Dog" live and take notice of his energetic dance moves. This video will help aid in the discussion below.

MEANINGFUL DISCUSSION

* Have you listened to Elvis Presley's music? Are you a fan? What was he famous for? (playing guitar, singing, good looks, shaking his hips, rock and roll, gospel music, acting in movies)
* Did you watch when Elvis Presley appeared on *The Ed Sullivan Show* in 1956? They only showed Elvis from the waist up that day because his hip movements were considered "obscene." Do you think his movements were inappropriate for television?
* What do you think it means to be a "hound dog"? (Someone who is whining all of the time and not being a good partner.)
* What does the song mean by "you ain't never caught a rabbit"? (This "hound dog" is not doing his job!)
* Did you ever date someone who could be described as a "hound dog"?

HOW GREAT THOU ART

SONG: *"How Great Thou Art"*
COMPOSERS/WRITERS: *Carl G. Boberg (writer), Stuart K. Hine (translator/writer)*
ARTIST(S): *Various Artists*
YEAR(S) RELEASED: *1885/1949*

ADDITIONAL INFORMATION

Carl G. Boberg, a Swedish preacher, wrote the poem *O Store Gud* in 1885. Later the poem was set to the tune of an old Swedish melody. This song was later translated into Russian. Years later, Stuart K. Hine, a missionary, heard the Russian version while in Poland. Hine later went on to translate the hymn into English, adding some original verses of his own as well and creating his own arrangement of the melody. Stuart Hine's version of "How Great Thou Art" was published in 1949 and became increasingly popular due to its frequent performances during the Billy Graham crusades. It has been recorded by numerous artists.

ENGAGED LISTENING

The lyrics of this song are well-known to many. Encourage your loved one to sing along as you listen together.

MEANINGFUL DISCUSSION

* What is this hymn about? (The greatness of God as seen in His creation and in His Son's ultimate sacrifice on the cross for us.)

* What specifically does the hymn mention as signs of God's greatness? (the stars, the rolling thunder, the woods, the forest glades, the birds singing, mountains, brooks, the gentle breeze, the universe, Jesus' death on the cross and resurrection, the coming of Christ to take believers home to heaven)

* What are some aspects of nature that remind you of the greatness of God?

* What else in your life personally inspires you to acknowledge the greatness of God?

(HOW MUCH IS) THAT DOGGIE IN THE WINDOW?

SONG: *"(How Much Is) That Doggie in the Window?"*
COMPOSERS/WRITERS: *Bob Merrill (composer)*
ARTIST(S): *Patti Page*
YEAR(S) RELEASED: *1953*

ADDITIONAL INFORMATION

This song topped the charts in both the United States and the United Kingdom the year it was released. Patti Page's version topped the United States charts while it was Lita Roza's version that topped charts in the United Kingdom.

ENGAGED LISTENING

Hold your loved one's hands and sway side to side with the gentle beat of this song. If your loved one has a mischievous sense of humor, encourage him or her to make dramatic or varied "barking" sounds with you where appropriate in the song. If you are able, share photographs of your loved one's pets or your pets (both past and present) to assist with the discussion below.

MEANINGFUL DISCUSSION

* What kind of store is the singer of this song visiting? (pet shop)

* What kinds of pets are listed in this song? (doggie, bunny, kitty, parrot, fishies) What are some other animals that people like to have as pets? (Prompt with examples as needed, such as hamster, guinea pig, turtle, mouse, snake, gerbil, lizard, horse, etc.)

* Did you ever have a pet? What kind of pet was it? When did you have this pet? (Prompt with examples as needed, such as childhood, while raising children, as an older adult, etc.)

* What was your pet's name? What can you tell me about him/her? What made your pet special?

* What were some of your favorite things to do with your pet? (Prompt with examples as needed, such as pet it, go for a walk, scratch behind the ears, brush its fur, feed it treats, play fetch, cuddle, etc.)

* Did you ever have any other pets? What kind(s) of other pets did you have?

I CAN SEE CLEARLY NOW

SONG: *"I Can See Clearly Now"*
COMPOSERS/WRITERS: *Johnny Nash (writer)*
ARTIST(S): *Johnny Nash*
YEAR(S) RELEASED: *1972*

ADDITIONAL INFORMATION

Johnny Nash is a Texas singer-songwriter whose music is known for its reggae influence. "I Can See Clearly Now" was number one on the *Billboard* charts for four weeks the year it was released. The song has appeared in various films and Jimmy Cliff released a famous cover of the song in 1993.

ENGAGED LISTENING

Encourage your loved one to sway side to side and clap to one side and then the other as you listen to this song together.

MEANINGFUL DISCUSSION

* What does "I can see clearly now the rain is gone" mean? (Life is looking up after a challenging time.)

* What is this song about? (This song is a hopeful look at better times after surviving a difficult period of some sort.)

* Tell me about a time you survived a challenging period in your life and how you felt after getting through it.

* Is your life in a "sunny" time or a "rainy" time right now? Why? Ask your loved one if there is anything you can do to help make the day better or make it "sunny."

* How does this song make you feel?

* The singer tells the listener to "look all around, there's nothing but blue skies." Have you ever experienced a time where everything in your life felt like it was going well? Tell me about it.

I COULD HAVE DANCED ALL NIGHT

SONG: *"I Could Have Danced All Night"*
COMPOSERS/WRITERS: *Frederick Loewe (music), Alan Jay Lerner (lyrics)*
ARTIST(S): *Julie Andrews, Marni Nixon*
YEAR(S) RELEASED: *1956*

ADDITIONAL INFORMATION

"I Could Have Danced All Night" is from the Broadway musical *My Fair Lady*. The musical won the Tony Award for "Best Musical" in 1957. Later, it was the basis for the 1964 film of the same name, which starred Audrey Hepburn and Rex Harrison and won eight Oscars. The storyline is based on the play *Pygmalion* (1913) by George Bernard Shaw. It tells the story of professor Higgins and his attempt to turn an unpolished, lower class girl, Eliza, into a proper-speaking lady. His tutoring is a success and Eliza passes for a princess at a ball. Though initially, Higgins treats Eliza with little respect and as a mere experiment, he eventually falls in love with her.

ENGAGED LISTENING

Hold your loved one's hands and help him or her to dance along with this song as you listen together.

MEANINGFUL DISCUSSION

* Do (did) you enjoy dancing? Was there ever a time you could have or did go dancing all night?

* What kind of dancing do you enjoy? What other styles of dance are there? (Prompt with suggestions as needed, such as ballroom dancing, the Charleston, swing dancing, the jitterbug, tango, the waltz, the twist, country line dancing, square dancing, Texas two-step, ballet, etc.)

* The singer wants to dance all night because she is so happy and in love. Does being very happy or in love make you want to dance? What are some other ways you tend to express joy and love?

* Who was someone special you liked to dance with? Was he or she a good dancer, or did you enjoy dancing together simply because you cared about each other?

* What are some special occasions that often include dancing? (Prompt with suggestions as needed, such as prom, weddings, a ball, parties, going out on New Year's Eve, etc.)

I GOT RHYTHM

SONG: *"I Got Rhythm"*
COMPOSERS/WRITERS: *George Gershwin (music), Ira Gershwin (lyrics)*
ARTIST(S): *Ethel Merman, Judy Garland, Gene Kelly, Ella Fitzgerald*
YEAR(S) RELEASED: *1930*

ADDITIONAL INFORMATION

George Gershwin and his brother Ira wrote the hit "I Got Rhythm" for the musical *Girl Crazy*, which starred Ethel Merman and opened on Broadway in the fall of 1930. On opening night, this song was a true showstopper as Merman literally stopped the show and had to repeat the now famous song several times. George Gershwin said (in 1933) that this song was his favorite out of all of the show tunes he had ever written. The song went on to become a very popular jazz standard and various renditions have been released by numerous artists over the years.

ENGAGED LISTENING

This song is excellent for dancing. Encourage your loved one to dance along with you as you listen together. Hold his or her hands to help your loved one move along with the beat or encourage him or her to imitate a variety of movements such as tapping toes, moving alternating shoulders up and down, moving side to side with the rhythm, or kicking as if in a chorus line.

MEANINGFUL DISCUSSION

* What does the singer say he or she's "got" in the song? (rhythm, music, my man/my gal, daisies, green pastures, sweet dreams, starlight)

* How does the singer feel about what he or she has? (Prompt with suggestions as needed, such as happy, content, satisfied, etc.)

* What do you have that makes you feel happy? (Prompt with examples as needed, such as friends, family, music, favorite hobbies, sunshine, etc.)

* What is something good that you have and are enjoying today?

I'M GONNA WASH THAT
MAN RIGHT OUTA MY HAIR

SONG: *"I'm Gonna Wash That Man Right Outa My Hair"*
COMPOSERS/WRITERS: *Richard Rodgers (music), Oscar Hammerstein II (lyrics)*
ARTIST(S): *Mary Martin, Mitzi Gaynor*
YEAR(S) RELEASED: *1949*

ADDITIONAL INFORMATION

This song was written for the Broadway musical *South Pacific*, which opened in 1949. It tells the story of a young Navy nurse, Nelly, and her older French suitor, Emile de Becque. Nelly sings this song as she shampoos her hair, insisting that she is over her relationship with him, however, they end up happily together at the end of the musical.

ENGAGED LISTENING

Encourage your loved one to move along with this upbeat song by tapping his or her toes (up and down or side to side) and then moving his or her shoulders up and down. Sway side to side during slower sections.

MEANINGFUL DISCUSSION

* What does "I'm gonna wash that man right outa my hair" mean? (end the relationship, get rid of him, "send him on his way," etc.)

* Does this song suggest any regrets over ending the relationship?

* Did you ever end a relationship with no regrets? What made ending that relationship an easy decision? Is it sometimes hard to end a relationship, even if you know it is the right decision?

* Although the singer cheerfully declares she is ending this relationship, she happily agrees to marry him by the end of the musical. Did you ever rekindle a previously ended relationship? How did the relationship go the second time around?

I'M LOOKING OVER A FOUR LEAF CLOVER

SONG: *"I'm Looking Over a Four Leaf Clover"*
COMPOSERS/WRITERS: *Mort Dixon (lyrics), Harry M. Woods (music)*
ARTIST(S): *Nick Lucas (1927 artist), Art Mooney (1948 artist)*
YEAR(S) RELEASED: *1927 (original), 1948 (revival)*

ADDITIONAL INFORMATION

This song is commonly associated with the *Merrie Melodies* cartoons, a series of short comedic films produced by Warner Bros. between 1931 and 1969. It was featured in several of the cartoons in the series.

ENGAGED LISTENING

If you have access to the Internet, find a picture of three and four leaf clovers to show your loved one to aid in the discussion below.

MEANINGFUL DISCUSSION

* What is special about a four leaf clover? (Most clovers have three leaves, so a four leaf clover is unusual. Four leaf clovers are also considered to bring good luck.)

* Have you ever found a four leaf clover? Did it bring you good luck?

* What does the song say the four leaves represent? (sunshine, rain, roses, somebody I adore)

* The song says the four leaf clover was initially overlooked. Do you think it's easy to sometimes overlook good things in life? What are some of the small blessings in your life right now?

* What are some other things besides four leaf clovers that are considered to be lucky? (Prompt with examples as needed, such as lucky rabbit foot, good luck pigs, a penny found heads-side-up, horseshoe, etc.)

IN THE GARDEN

SONG: *"In the Garden"*
COMPOSERS/WRITERS: *C. Austin Miles (writer)*
ARTIST(S): *Various Artists*
YEAR(S) RELEASED: *1912/1913*

ADDITIONAL INFORMATION

"In the Garden" references Mary Magdalene's experience at Jesus' tomb after his crucifixion and burial. Upon finding the tomb empty, she sees someone she thinks is the gardener until she hears Him, her risen Lord, call her by name. This song captures her joy in the garden and also suggests the joy and comfort Christians experience in talking with the Lord and walking in His ways. This hymn was written by C. Austin Miles, who left his job as a pharmacist at the age of 24 to focus on writing hymns and publishing music.

ENGAGED LISTENING

Encourage your loved one to relax and take deep breaths as you listen to this song together. If you have access to the Internet, look up the famous poem "Footprints" to aid the discussion below.

MEANINGFUL DISCUSSION

* The chorus of this hymn says the joy of walking and talking with God is unlike any other joy. Do you think that is true?

* This hymn describes being able to connect with God in a concrete way, through walking and talking with Him. Do you think this accurately describes the Christian life? Do you feel God's presence in your life? Can you tell me about it?

* Is there comfort in knowing that God tells us "we are His own" or that we belong to Him? What does it mean to belong to God?

* How do you connect with God and feel His presence? (Prompt with suggestions as needed, such as praying, reading the Bible, listening to or singing hymns, talking with other believers, attending a service, etc.)

* Read the poem "Footprints" aloud to your loved one. Do you think the author of the poem and the singer in the song feel similarly about walking with God and taking comfort in His presence?

IN THE GOOD OLD SUMMERTIME

SONG: *"In the Good Old Summertime"*
COMPOSERS/WRITERS: *George Evans (music), Ren Shields (lyrics)*
ARTIST(S): *Nat King Cole*
YEAR(S) RELEASED: *1902*

ADDITIONAL INFORMATION

This song first appeared in the Broadway show *The Defender*, which ran at the Herald Square Theater during the summer of 1902. The song was also featured in a Judy Garland movie of the same name released in 1949.

ENGAGED LISTENING

The chorus of this song is very well-known. Encourage your loved one to sing it along with you as you listen together.

MEANINGFUL DISCUSSION

* What comes to mind when you think of summertime?

* Do you like summer? What do you like best about summer?

* What is the weather like in the summertime? (Prompt with examples as needed, such as sunny, hot, longer days, less rain, white clouds, blue skies, etc.)

* What are some of your favorite summertime activities? (Prompt with examples as needed, such as swimming, baseball, fishing, camping, vacations, the beach, picnics, barbecues, golf, tennis, fireworks, gardening, family reunions, sitting outside, jumping rope, etc.)

* What are some of your favorite summertime foods? (Prompt with examples as needed, such as ice cream, watermelon, corn on the cob, lemonade, iced tea, potato salad, cold beer, etc.)

* Many people think about finding love and dating or going steady in the summertime. Did you ever have a summer love? What sort of things did you enjoy doing together during the summer? (Prompt with examples as needed, such as picnics, drive-in movies, long romantic walks, concerts in the park, summer dances, etc.)

IN THE STILL OF THE NIGHT

SONG: *"In the Still of the Night"*
COMPOSERS/WRITERS: *Fred Parris (writer)*
ARTIST(S): *The Five Satins*
YEAR(S) RELEASED: *1956*

ADDITIONAL INFORMATION

"In the Still of the Night" (sometimes spelled 'Nite') is the only song to have charted on the *Billboard* Hot 100 three separate times with the same version by the same artist each time (1956, 1960, 1961). The lyrics during the bridge ("doo wop, doo wah") make it one of two songs that can claim to have inspired the term "doo-wop" to describe this genre of music. Written by Fred Parris while he was in the Army, it is ranked number 90 on the *Rolling Stone*'s list of "500 Greatest Songs of All Time," despite only reaching a peak of number 24 on the national pop charts when it was released.

ENGAGED LISTENING

Sway and clap from side to side with the rhythm of this song and encourage your loved one to do the same.

MEANINGFUL DISCUSSION

* Do you remember when doo-wop first became popular? Are you a fan of doo-wop music?

* Have you ever held someone and promised to never let them go? Who was it? How long were you together?

* This song is a popular song for slow dancing. Do (did) you like to dance?

* What does the song mean by "the still of the night"? (A very peaceful time of evening, when things are quiet and calm, different from the sometimes hurried and distracted pace of day.) Is it easier to focus on and enjoy being with someone you love "in the still of the night"?

IN THE SWEET BY AND BY

SONG: *"In the Sweet By and By"*
COMPOSERS/WRITERS: *S. Fillmore Bennett (lyrics), Joseph P. Webster (music)*
ARTIST(S): *Various Artists*
YEAR(S) RELEASED: *1868*

ADDITIONAL INFORMATION

"In the Sweet By and By" is a Christian hymn that was originally composed in 1868 and remains popular today. S. Fillmore Bennett and Joseph P. Webster worked together in a village in Wisconsin. One day, appearing flustered, Webster walked to where Bennett was working. Bennett asked, "What is the matter now?" Webster replied, "It's no matter, it will be all right by and by." Bennett exclaimed, "In the sweet by and by!" and began writing the lyrics to the hymn we know today. "In the Sweet By and By" has become a gospel standard and some notable recordings include Johnny Cash, Dolly Parton, Nat King Cole, Willie Nelson, and Loretta Lynn.

ENGAGED LISTENING

The chorus is the most familiar part of this song. Encourage your loved one to sing with you during each chorus, starting with "In the sweet by and by."

MEANINGFUL DISCUSSION

* What is this song about? (heaven)
* This hymn describes heaven as "a land that is fairer than day." What comes to mind when you think about heaven?
* The chorus says, "we shall meet on that beautiful shore." What does this sentiment mean? (We shall meet again in heaven.) What do you think about this description of heaven?
* How does this hymn make you feel? (Prompt with suggestions as needed, such as peaceful, comforted, encouraged, calm, reassured, blessed, etc.)

IT IS WELL WITH MY SOUL

SONG: *"It Is Well with My Soul"*
COMPOSERS/WRITERS: *Horatio Spafford (lyrics), Philip Bliss (music)*
ARTIST(S): *Various Artists*
YEAR(S) RELEASED: *1873/1876*

ADDITIONAL INFORMATION

Spafford was a successful businessman who lost everything during the Great Chicago Fire in 1871. Then, in 1873, his wife Anna and their four daughters were crossing the Atlantic bound for Europe when their ship was struck by another vessel and sank in 12 minutes. Only Anna survived, sending her husband the telegram, "Saved alone." Spafford took the next boat out and penned the lyrics as he passed the spot where the ship carrying his daughters went down. Philip Bliss, a family friend, wrote the tune and the song was published in 1876.

ENGAGED LISTENING

The chorus of this hymn is very well-known. Encourage your loved one to sing it along with you as you listen together.

MEANINGFUL DISCUSSION

* What do the words "it is well with my soul" mean?

* The lyrics say that the Lord enables us to say "it is well with my soul" no matter what our circumstances are in life. Do you think this is true?

* The lyrics offer reassurance that no matter what happens in this life, we have hope of eternal salvation in Christ because He died for our sins. Does that thought bring you hope even in the midst of sorrow or challenging times?

* Was there ever a time that it was hard to feel peace or the presence of God? How did you get through this time? Were you able to regain or renew your faith?

* Did you ever experience the peace of the Lord in the midst of a difficult time? Can you tell me about it?

ITSY BITSY TEENIE WEENIE YELLOW POLKA DOT BIKINI

SONG: *"Itsy Bitsy Teenie Weenie Yellow Polka Dot Bikini"*
COMPOSERS/WRITERS: *Paul Vance & Lee Pockriss (writers)*
ARTIST(S): *Brian Hyland*
YEAR(S) RELEASED: 1960

ADDITIONAL INFORMATION

The famous recording by Brian Hyland, who was only 16 years old at the time, became a number one hit on the *Billboard* Hot 100 chart in the United States and made it to the top ten in both the United Kingdom and New Zealand. Several other versions of this song emerged after the original became a hit in the United States. The titles include: "Itsy Bitsy Teenie Weenie Honolulu Strand-Bikini"(German), "Itsi Bitsi Petit Bikini" (French), a parody by Buddy Hackett of the same name, and even a version in response called "Poor Begonia," which sings about how "poor Begonia caught pneumonia."

ENGAGED LISTENING

Encourage your loved one to dance along to the song. Some suggested movements include lifting shoulders up and down (together and one at a time), doing the twist, and moving arms in a swimming motion. You can also count and mimic the phrase "1, 2, 3, 4, tell the people what she wore" each time it is said in the song. If you have access to the Internet, look up pictures of bathing suits from different decades and compare styles to aid in the discussion below.

MEANINGFUL DISCUSSION

* The singer talks about a girl who is "afraid to come out of the locker" after putting on her new bathing suit for the first time. Have you ever felt nervous or self-conscious about a new outfit or bathing suit? How did you handle it? Did you wrap yourself in a blanket or towel? Did you decide to change? Did you go out confidently?

* (If you have pictures to reference from the engaged listening) Would you wear any of these bathing suits? Why or why not?

* What kind of bathing suit did you wear to the beach, pool, lake, etc.? Do you prefer your bathing suit to be fashionable or functional? Have you ever worn a bikini?

* When you go to the beach, do you enjoy swimming or do you prefer to sit on the shore?

I'VE BEEN WORKING ON THE RAILROAD

SONG: *"I've Been Working on the Railroad"*
COMPOSERS/WRITERS: *Traditional/Unknown*
ARTIST(S): *Pete Seeger, John Denver*
YEAR(S) RELEASED: *Traditional/Unknown*

ADDITIONAL INFORMATION

"I've Been Working on the Railroad" is one of the most famous American folk songs of all time. There are various theories as to its origins. Some suggest it came from an old Irish hymn, while others suggest it came from an African American spiritual. The verse starting with "Someone's in the kitchen with Dinah" was actually absorbed from a separate folk song altogether. Regardless of its origins, the song describes the long work days associated with building the railroad, and recalls an important, though grueling, time in American history.

ENGAGED LISTENING

This song, with its strong consistent beat, is perfect for movement. Encourage your loved one to march with you as you listen and sing along together, lifting each leg as high as possible. You can also encourage your loved one to clap or pat his or her knees with the beat.

MEANINGFUL DISCUSSION

* This song describes long, hard days working to build a railroad. Did you ever have a job that was really challenging? What was the job and what made it difficult?

* Some jobs are challenging physically and some jobs are challenging mentally. Did you ever have a job that was physically challenging? What was it? Did you ever have a job that was mentally challenging? What was it?

* Of all the jobs you've worked, what was your favorite? Why did you enjoy that job so much? What was your least favorite? Why?

* This song describes the building of a railroad. Now we have railroads that run throughout the United States. Have you ever ridden on a train? Where did you catch the train? Where did you take the train?

* Trains have become less popular for travel. What other modes of travel are popular today?

I WANT TO HOLD YOUR HAND

SONG: *"I Want to Hold Your Hand"*
COMPOSERS/WRITERS: *John Lennon & Paul McCartney (writers)*
ARTIST(S): *The Beatles*
YEAR(S) RELEASED: *1963*

ADDITIONAL INFORMATION

"I Want to Hold Your Hand" was the first Beatles song to become popular in the United States and it became a number one hit in February of 1964. Shortly after the song's success, the Beatles had their first United States television performance on *The Ed Sullivan Show* singing this song. "I Want to Hold Your Hand" was number one on the *Billboard* Hot 100 chart and held this spot for seven weeks until it was replaced by another Beatles hit, "She Loves You." In 2013, *Billboard* magazine named "I Want to Hold Your Hand" as the "44th biggest hit of all time."

ENGAGED LISTENING

While listening to this song, encourage your loved one to clap along with the rhythm. If you have access to the Internet, search for a video clip of the Beatles performing this song for the first time in the United States on *The Ed Sullivan Show*.

MEANINGFUL DISCUSSION

- This song is about the excitement and happiness you get from holding someone's hand. When someone you care about holds your hand, how does it make you feel?

- Do you remember the first time your sweetheart held your hand?

- When you first started dating someone you cared about, did you make the first move to hold hands or did your date?

- What are some other gestures of affection you can do for someone you care about? (Prompt with examples as needed, such as hugs, kisses, cuddles, sending flowers, giving a small gift or thoughtful card, a reassuring pat on the back, etc.)

JAMBALAYA (ON THE BAYOU)

SONG: *"Jambalaya (On the Bayou)"*
COMPOSERS/WRITERS: *Hank Williams (writer)*
ARTIST(S): *Hank Williams*
YEAR(S) RELEASED: *1952*

ADDITIONAL INFORMATION

Although Hank Willams is credited with writing the hit "Jambalaya," the melody originally came from a Cajun French song known as "Grand Texas." The song peaked at number one on the *Billboard* Country chart and number 20 on the *Billboard* Pop chart. It has since been recorded by numerous artists.

ENGAGED LISTENING

Encourage your loved one to tap his or her toes and heels along with you as you listen to this song together. If you have access to the Internet, find a few pictures of bayous and the foods mentioned in the song (jambalaya, crawfish pie, gumbo) to share with your loved one and aid in the discussion below.

MEANINGFUL DISCUSSION

* How would you describe the mood of this song? (Prompt with suggestions as needed, such as cheerful, fun, easy-going, happy, content, etc.)

* The song describes getting together with friends and family for a fun time. What are your get-togethers with family and friends like? What are some things you do together to have a fun time?

* The song discusses having fun "on the bayou." What is a bayou? (A bayou is a slow-moving or still body of water, typically a marshy or boggy inlet or outlet of a river or lake. Bayous typically are found in the South and Gulf States.) Have you ever been to a bayou?

* What is Jambalaya? (a Creole/Louisiana-French dish that resembles a thick stew) What ingredients are typically included in Jambalaya? (rice, ham, sausage, chicken, seafood, herbs and spices, tomatoes, onions, and peppers) What are some other types of Creole food? (Prompt with examples as needed, such as crawfish etouffee, gumbo, etc.) Do you enjoy Creole food? Have you ever made Jambalaya? If so, what do you like to put in it?

JESUS LOVES ME

SONG: *"Jesus Loves Me"*
COMPOSERS/WRITERS: *Anna Bartlett Warner (lyrics), William Batchelder Bradbury (music/chorus)*
ARTIST(S): *Various Artists*
YEAR(S) RELEASED: *1860/1862*

ADDITIONAL INFORMATION

This hymn was originally written as a poem by Anna Bartlett Warner in 1860 as part of a novel by her sister Susan Warner. In the novel, the words were spoken to comfort a child who was dying. In 1862, William Batchelder Bradbury added a tune to the poem as well as the chorus. The song is one of the most popular Christian hymns around the world, and has been covered by many artists including Ray Stevens, Whitney Houston, Rosemary Clooney, and Dionne Warwick.

ENGAGED LISTENING

Hold your loved one's hand and encourage him or her to sing along with the chorus of the song: "Yes, Jesus loves me. Yes, Jesus loves me. Yes, Jesus loves me, the Bible tells me so."

MEANINGFUL DISCUSSION

* Did you learn this song as a child? Despite being written over 100 years ago, children are still learning this song today. Do you think there is something special about songs that are handed down from generation to generation? Did you teach this song to your children or grandchildren?

* Are you familiar with the Bible? What are your favorite books or passages?

* This song was written to be a comforting reminder of Jesus' love. What are some other things that you find comforting during a difficult time? (Prompt with examples as needed, such as prayer, reading the Bible, spending time with family, going to church, listening to music, singing, being outdoors, etc.)

* Did you ever hear or sing this song at church? What are some of your favorite hymns?

JOHNNY B. GOODE

SONG: *"Johnny B. Goode"*
COMPOSERS/WRITERS: *Chuck Berry (writer)*
ARTIST(S): *Chuck Berry*
YEAR(S) RELEASED: *1958*

ADDITIONAL INFORMATION

Chuck Berry wrote this song partly about himself. "Johnny B. Goode" is one of Chuck Berry's most famous songs, and is ranked number seven on *Rolling Stone*'s "500 Greatest Songs of All Time" list. It has been covered by many artists, and is considered one of the most recognizable songs in music history.

ENGAGED LISTENING

Encourage your loved one to tap his or her toes and clap his or her hands along with the verses of the song. During the chorus, encourage your loved one to sing along with you: "Go, go Johnny go, go…"

MEANINGFUL DISCUSSION

* This song is about a poor country boy who is extremely musically talented. What is something you're talented at? Did you ever consider pursuing it professionally? Why or why not?

* Have you ever wanted to be famous? Why or why not? What do you think it would be like to be instantly recognizable?

* Johnny B. Goode's mother encourages his musical talent in this song. Did your parents encourage you to develop your talents or special skills? How did they encourage you? (Prompt with suggestions as needed, such as paying for lessons or equipment, praise and words of encouragement, teaching or coaching you, etc.)

* Why do you think this song was so popular?

LEAN ON ME

SONG: *"Lean on Me"*
COMPOSERS/WRITERS: *Bill Withers (writer)*
ARTIST(S): *Bill Withers*
YEAR(S) RELEASED: *1972*

ADDITIONAL INFORMATION

Most everyone can identify with the lyrics of this song and it became popular due to its relatable subject matter. *Billboard* ranked "Lean on Me" at number seven for the top songs of 1972 and it appears at spot number 208 on *Rolling Stone*'s "500 Greatest Songs of All Time" list. In 2015, this song was performed when Bill Withers was inducted into the Rock and Roll Hall of Fame.

ENGAGED LISTENING

While listening to this song sit side by side (shoulder to shoulder) and sway with your loved one. Encourage him or her to sing along with the chorus, starting with "Lean on me…"

MEANINGFUL DISCUSSION

* The song says, "We all need somebody to lean on." Do you agree with this statement? Do you think it is easier to "share the load" when you have someone to talk to and help you through it?

* What are some reasons you might need someone to lean on? (Prompt with suggestions as needed, such as pain, illness, sorrow, challenges at work, needing help at home, carrying a burden, financial trouble, relationship challenges, etc.)

* Who comes to mind when you think of someone to lean on? Why is he or she such a good person to lean on?

* Sometimes, it can be hard to admit you need help or want someone to lean on. The singer suggests to "swallow your pride." Do you agree with this? Is it sometimes difficult to ask for help and share your problem?

* We all need friends we can lean on. Besides being there for you, what are some other qualities you look for in a friend?

LEAVING ON A JET PLANE

SONG: *"Leaving on a Jet Plane"*
COMPOSERS/WRITERS: *John Denver (writer)*
ARTIST(S): *Peter, Paul & Mary (1969); John Denver (1973)*
YEAR(S) RELEASED: *1969*

ADDITIONAL INFORMATION

"Leaving on a Jet Plane" was the fifth song John Denver ever wrote and became one of the biggest hits recorded by Peter, Paul & Mary. During an interview, John Denver said that this song does not remind him of an airplane as much as it does a "longing of having someone to love." Denver recorded a solo version of "Leaving on a Jet Plane" on his *Greatest Hits* album in 1973.

ENGAGED LISTENING

Encourage your loved one to sway with the rhythm of the song and sing along with the chorus.

MEANINGFUL DISCUSSION

* Have you ever had to travel without your family or spouse? If so, where were you going? How long were you gone? Was it hard to leave?

* What are some of the ways the song suggests saying goodbye before leaving on the jet plane? (kiss me, smile, ask that you wait for me, hold me, etc.) How do you say goodbye to someone you care about before a big trip? What are some ways you get ready for the trip?

* Do you like to travel alone or would you rather have someone with you? Why?

* Who is someone you enjoy traveling with? Why is he or she such a good travel companion?

* Have you ever traveled by plane? Do you like flying? Where are some of the places you've traveled to by plane?

LET IT BE

SONG: *"Let It Be"*
COMPOSERS/WRITERS: *Paul McCartney (writer)*
ARTIST(S): *The Beatles*
YEAR(S) RELEASED: *1970*

ADDITIONAL INFORMATION

While Aretha Franklin recorded and released her version of this song two months before the Beatles, the Beatles version is the most well-known, reaching number one on the charts in the United States and number two on the charts in the United Kingdom. "Let It Be" was the last single released by the Beatles before they announced their split. The song was inspired by a comforting dream Paul McCartney had of his mother, Mary, who had passed away when he was just 14 years old.

ENGAGED LISTENING

Encourage your loved one to relax and take deep breaths as you listen to the song together.

MEANINGFUL DISCUSSION

* How does this song make you feel? (Prompt with examples as needed, such as comforted, encouraged, reassured, calm, peaceful, etc.) What is it about the song that makes you feel that way?
* Paul McCartney's mother, Mary, passed away when he was 14 years old. Ten years later, after having a dream where she came to comfort him, he wrote this song. Is there someone in your life who is always there to comfort and reassure you when things are difficult?
* What does the refrain of the song say over and over? (let it be) What do you think "let it be" means?
* Is there anything in your life right now that is troubling you? Is this something that you can just "let it be"? What are some other ways to work through this trouble?

LET ME CALL YOU SWEETHEART

SONG: *"Let Me Call You Sweetheart"*
COMPOSERS/WRITERS: *Leo Friedman (music), Beth Slater Whitson (lyrics)*
ARTIST(S): *The Peerless Quartet, Bing Crosby*
YEAR(S) RELEASED: *1910*

ADDITIONAL INFORMATION

The sheet music for the classic love song "Let Me Call You Sweetheart" was published in 1910 and was first recorded by The Peerless Quartet. There have been many recordings of this song including a version by Laurel and Hardy in their 1938 comedic film *Swiss Miss*. Other notable artists include Patti Page, and Dean Martin and Kate Smith.

ENGAGED LISTENING

Hold your loved one's hands and sway side to side with the rhythm of the music as you encourage him or her to sing along with you.

MEANINGFUL DISCUSSION

* What are some other nicknames for a loved one besides sweetheart? (Prompt with examples as needed, such as honey, love, sugar, sweetie pie, pumpkin, babe, honey bunny, baby cakes, better half, etc.) What nicknames have you used for your sweetheart? Do (did) your sweetheart have any special pet names for you?

* Tell me about your sweetheart. What makes (made) him or her so special? (Prompt with examples as needed, such as kind, generous, trustworthy, handsome/beautiful, caring, funny, smart, good cook, fun to be with, energetic, encouraging, etc.)

LOVE ME TENDER

SONG: *"Love Me Tender"*

COMPOSERS/WRITERS: *George R. Poulton (music), William Whiteman Fosdick (lyrics) in 1861 for the song "Aura Lee;" Additional lyrics written by Elvis Presley & Vera Matson/Ken Darby 1956*

ARTIST(S): *Elvis Presley*

YEAR(S) RELEASED: *1956*

ADDITIONAL INFORMATION

Inspired by the 1861 song "Aura Lee," the song "Love Me Tender" was written for the 1956 movie of the same title. When Elvis was cast in the film, it was decided that he would sing a ballad, which was in contrast to his then-current musical style. The music director, Ken Darby, originally suggested they use the melody from "Aura Lee." It is said that Darby re-wrote the lyrics with Elvis, but he gave the credit to his wife, Vera Matson. *Love Me Tender* is a black and white Western that takes place at the end of the Civil War. This film was the first of many films starring Elvis.

ENGAGED LISTENING

If you have access to the Internet, find a younger and older picture of Elvis to use while listening to the song.

MEANINGFUL DISCUSSION

* Does the song remind you of anyone special? Who does it make you think of?

* This song is about a true love; how does the song describe that true love? Do you or did you have a true love who will always love you and who you will always love? What makes him or her your true love and so special?

* Referring to the pictures mentioned above, ask your loved one which version of Elvis he or she remembers the best. What do you remember about Elvis? (Prompt with examples as needed, such as: He became known as "Elvis the Pelvis" due to all his hip shaking; He was called "The King of Rock and Roll;" He was incredibly handsome; etc.) Do you enjoy his music? Why or why not?

* Did you see the film *Love Me Tender* or any of Elvis' other films?

* This song is still popular as a wedding song today. Did you have a special song at your wedding? What was it?

MOONLIGHT BAY

SONG: *"Moonlight Bay"*
COMPOSERS/WRITERS: *Edward Madden (lyrics), Percy Wenrich (music)*
ARTIST(S): *Doris Day, The American Quartet*
YEAR(S) RELEASED: *Released 1912 (published), 1951 (Doris Day version)*

ADDITIONAL INFORMATION

While originally published in 1912, this song has been covered by numerous artists over several decades. Most notably, Doris Day sang it in the movie *On Moonlight Bay* in 1951. The Beatles also recorded a version in 1963. Many versions of this song have been sung in the style of a barbershop quartet.

ENGAGED LISTENING

Hold your loved one's hands and gently sway side to side with the rhythm, imitating the gentle rocking motion of a boat.

MEANINGFUL DISCUSSION

* Have you ever been sailing? Have you ever been on a boat? In what kind of boat did you ride? (Prompt with examples as needed, such as small boat/big boat, motorboat, cruise ship, canoe, sailboat, row boat, etc.)

* Where did you go sailing/boat riding? (Prompt with examples as needed, such as ocean, lake, river, bay, or a specific location.)

* Did you like being out on the water? What do you remember about it?

* Do you like to be near the water? Have you ever been by the ocean/at the beach/by a lake? What do you like about the beach/being lakeside?

* What other kind of activities do you enjoy when you are by the water? (Prompt with examples as needed, such as swimming, fishing, collecting seashells, walking, sunbathing, tubing/floating down the river, snorkeling, water skiing, etc.)

* This song describes being out on the water at night in the moonlight with someone special. Does that sound like a romantic date to you?

* Tell me about a romantic date you took with your sweetheart. Where did you go? What did you do?

* If you were to take someone on a romantic date today, what would you do?

MOON RIVER

SONG: *"Moon River"*
COMPOSERS/WRITERS: *Henry Mancini (music), Johnny Mercer (lyrics)*
ARTIST(S): *Audrey Hepburn, Andy Williams*
YEAR(S) RELEASED: *Released 1961*

ADDITIONAL INFORMATION

The song "Moon River" debuted in the film *Breakfast at Tiffany's* in 1961, performed by Audrey Hepburn. Johnny Mercer's lyrics were inspired by a river in Savannah, Georgia where his childhood home is located. The river was originally known as "Back River," however, the name was changed to "Moon River" after the song's success. One of the most famous recordings of "Moon River" is by Andy Williams, who used it as his television show's theme song. This song won an Oscar for "Best Song" in 1962 as well as Grammy awards for "Record of the Year," "Song of the Year," and "Best Arrangement."

ENGAGED LISTENING

For this song, encourage your loved one to sway slowly from side to side with you. You can also encourage your loved one to take slow deep breaths with the rhythm of the song.

MEANINGFUL DISCUSSION

- Have you ever spent time by a river? If so, what kinds of activities did you enjoy there? (Prompt with examples as needed, such as swimming, fishing, sailing, walking, having a picnic, skipping stones, wading, etc.) In this song, the lyrics mention the river is "wider than a mile." How big were the river(s) where you spent time?

- Have you ever seen the reflection of the moon on the water in the evening? If so, how did it make you feel? (Prompt with suggestions as needed, such as relaxed, calm, content, romantic, scared, etc.)

- This song sings about "two drifters off to see the world" and later says, "we're after the same rainbow's end." Is the song about traveling or romance? (Discuss how the song describes "two drifters," which could refer to people whose home is only with each other and "after the same rainbows end" could describe the idea that they are searching for the same things in life.)

- Do (did) you have a partner in life who always made you feel at home? Did you both want the same things in life? If so, what are (were) they? If not, what different things did you want?

MY BONNIE LIES OVER THE OCEAN

SONG: *"My Bonnie Lies Over the Ocean"*
COMPOSERS/WRITERS: *Traditional/Unknown*
ARTIST(S): *Mitch Miller*
YEAR(S) RELEASED: *Traditional, 1881 First Known Printing*

ADDITIONAL INFORMATION

"My Bonnie Lies Over the Ocean" is actually a traditional Scottish folk song. However, it has been popular in the United States for decades and is often included with American folk songs.

ENGAGED LISTENING

The rhythm of this song emulates the gentle ebb and flow of the ocean. Encourage your loved one to sway from side to side as you listen together.

MEANINGFUL DISCUSSION

* What do you think of when you think of the ocean or the sea? (Prompt with examples as needed, such as the smell of salt water, the sound of the waves, the feeling of sand between your toes, warm sunshine, cool water, the sound of seagulls, searching for seashells, ocean breezes, the smell of suntan lotion, etc.)

* Do you like to be by the ocean or the sea? Why or why not?

* When you imagine the ocean, do you see large crashing waves or calm waters? Do you like to be out on the water or do you prefer to be on the shore?

* The singer of this song misses "Bonnie," who is far away across the sea. Have you ever been long distance from a sweetheart? How long were you apart and why? What were some ways you and your sweetheart stayed in touch? (Prompt with examples as needed, such as letters, phone calls, etc.) Discuss how the technology of today has changed long-distance separations and how emails can instantly deliver "letters" anywhere in the world, long-distance and international phone calls are easy and affordable, and now you can even place video calls over the computer to anyone anywhere in the world.

* Do you have family or friends who live far away now? What are some of the ways you keep in touch?

MY FAVORITE THINGS

SONG: *"My Favorite Things"*
COMPOSERS/WRITERS: *Oscar Hammerstein II (lyrics), Richard Rogers (music)*
ARTIST(S): *Julie Andrews*
YEAR(S) RELEASED: *1959 (Broadway), 1965 (film)*

ADDITIONAL INFORMATION

"My Favorite Things" was originally performed by Mary Martin in the 1959 Broadway production of *The Sound of Music*, and was performed in the movie version of the same name in 1965 by Julie Andrews. Andrews's version is widely considered to be the definitive version of the song. In the original Broadway musical, the song was sung by Maria right before she is sent to be the von Trapp family's governess, but in the movie, the song was sung with the children during a thunderstorm. The song was ranked as number 64 on the American Film Institute's "100 Years…100 Songs" list in 2004. It is also popular during the holiday season. It has been covered by several other artists including John Coltrane, Barbra Streisand, Andy Williams, Diana Ross and the Supremes, and Tony Bennett.

ENGAGED LISTENING

While listening to this song, have your loved one look around his or her room. Ask him or her if there are any objects (blankets/quilts, china, family possessions, books, pictures, photographs, etc.), sights (looking out the window), or sounds that remind him or her of favorite things.

MEANINGFUL DISCUSSION

* What are some of the "favorite things" listed in the song? (raindrops on roses, whiskers on kittens, copper kettles, doorbells, sleigh bells, apple strudel, snowflakes, wild geese, cream colored ponies, etc.). Are any of these your favorite things as well?

* What are some of your favorite things? (Ask about favorite hobbies, objects around the room, and activities.)

* Some of the "favorite things" the song mentions are comforting foods. What are your favorite comfort foods? (Prompt with examples as needed, such as apple pie, meatloaf with mashed potatoes, chicken pot pie, chili, chicken and dumplings, enchiladas, macaroni and cheese, fried chicken, soup, tea, cookies, ice cream, etc.)

* The song mentions thinking of favorite things to feel better when something unpleasant happens. What else can you do to feel better when you're feeling sad? (Prompt with examples as needed, such as sing, listen to a favorite song, laugh with a loved one, take a walk, pray, talk to a friend, enjoy a favorite hobby, watch a movie, read a book, etc.)

MY GIRL

SONG: *"My Girl"*
COMPOSERS/WRITERS: *Smokey Robinson (lyrics), Ronald White (music)*
ARTIST(S): *The Temptations*
YEAR(S) RELEASED: *1964*

ADDITIONAL INFORMATION

"My Girl" was the Temptations' first number one single in the United States and is now considered their signature song. Smokey Robinson wrote the lyrics while he was married, but he said that the song was "written with all the women in the world in mind." The previous year, Robinson wrote the song "My Guy," which was a female perspective on the same sentiment of unconditional love. The Temptations were originally a five-man performing group that formed in Detroit, Michigan in 1961 and brought together two local groups, "The Primes" and "The Distants."

ENGAGED LISTENING

While listening to the song, snap your fingers, clap your hands or pat your lap along with the beat and encourage your loved one to do the same.

MEANINGFUL DISCUSSION

* What sorts of things does the singer have? (sunshine, honey, riches) Why does he feel so blessed? (He has a girl that he loves very much.) Have you ever loved someone the way the singer talks about his girl? Tell me about him or her! Did he or she love you too? Did you date? How long were you together? Did you get married?

* The singer says he doesn't need money, fortune, or fame because he has love. Is the singer being realistic or romantic? Do you think that love is all you need?

* Some have interpreted this song to describe a parent/daughter relationship. Do (did) you have a daughter? What makes (made) her special?

OH! SUSANNA

SONG: *"Oh! Susanna"*
COMPOSERS/WRITERS: *Stephen Foster (writer)*
ARTIST(S): *Pete Seeger/Various Artists*
YEAR(S) RELEASED: *1848*

ADDITIONAL INFORMATION

"Oh! Susanna" was written by Stephen Foster, commonly known as the father of American music. It was his first big hit, written when he was 21 years old. Foster went on to write over 200 songs, many of which are now considered quintessential to American folk music. The song was an unofficial anthem of the California Gold Rush and remained popular throughout the Civil War. It is still popular today. The publishers paid Foster $100 for the song.

ENGAGED LISTENING

Encourage your loved one to move along with you as you listen together. Suggested movements include: tap your toes, pat the beat on your knees, clap your hands, and march in place.

MEANINGFUL DISCUSSION

- Where is the singer of this song from? (Alabama) Where is he going? (Louisiana)

- Why is the singer traveling to Louisiana? (to see his true love, Susanna)

- Have you ever traveled a long way to see your true love? Tell me about the trip you took. Why were you and your true love apart? Did the trip to see your true love seem long or short?

- American folk songs, such as "Oh! Susanna," get passed down from generation to generation, meaning people of all ages know and can sing them. What other folk songs can you name?

OH, WHAT A BEAUTIFUL MORNIN'

SONG: *"Oh, What a Beautiful Mornin'"*
COMPOSERS/WRITERS: *Oscar Hammerstein II (lyrics), Richard Rodgers (music)*
ARTIST(S): *Alfred Drake, Gordon MacRae*
YEAR(S) RELEASED: *1943*

ADDITIONAL INFORMATION

This song was written for the musical *Oklahoma!* and is the first song at the start of the show. It has been covered by several artists including Frank Sinatra, Ray Charles, Peggy Lee, and James Taylor. *Oklahoma!* was the first musical written by the famed Rodgers and Hammerstein team. A film version of *Oklahoma!* was released in 1955. *Oklahoma!* is considered by many to have set the standard for American musical theater.

ENGAGED LISTENING

While listening to this song, encourage your loved one to sway from side to side during each chorus, which starts, "Oh, what a beautiful mornin'." If you have Internet access, look at pictures of beautiful sunrises and morning land-scapes as you listen to this song with your loved one.

MEANINGFUL DISCUSSION

* Have you ever seen the musical *Oklahoma!*? Did you enjoy it? Where did you see it?

* Have you ever been to Oklahoma? What do you remember about it?

* What's your idea of a beautiful morning? Do you prefer it to be cool or warm? Sunny or cloudy?

* Are you a morning person? What time do you like to get up in the morning? What are some of your favorite morning routines? (Prompt with examples as needed, such as a cup of coffee, watching television in pajamas, taking a bath/shower, looking out the window to see what the day is like, greeting loved ones, reading the paper, etc.)

* Do you think having a beautiful or good morning can set the stage for the whole day to be good?

* What are some things you can do to ensure your day gets off to a good start?

ON THE GOOD SHIP LOLLIPOP

SONG: *"On the Good Ship Lollipop"*
COMPOSERS/WRITERS: *Sidney Clare (lyrics), Richard A. Whiting (music)*
ARTIST(S): *Shirley Temple*
YEAR(S) RELEASED: *1934*

ADDITIONAL INFORMATION

The song "On the Good Ship Lollipop" was first performed by Shirley Temple in the movie *Bright Eyes* in 1934, and became her signature song. Shirley Temple was only six years old when this song was released, and she received a special "pint-sized" Academy Award for the movie.

ENGAGED LISTENING

Encourage your loved one to tap his or her toes and heels along with you as you listen to the song together. If you have access to the Internet, search for a picture of Shirley Temple or a video of her performance of this song in the film *Bright Eyes* to aid in the discussion below.

MEANINGFUL DISCUSSION

* What desserts are mentioned in the song? (lollipop, bonbons, peppermints, lemonade, Cracker Jack, chocolate bar, Tootsie Roll, devil's food cake) What are your favorite desserts? (Prompt with examples as needed, such as ice cream, cake, pie, cookies, fudge, chocolate, pudding, Jell-O, etc.)

* Shirley Temple was only six years old when she sang this song. What were your favorite desserts when you were younger? Are they the same or different than your favorites now? (Prompt with examples of child-friendly desserts as needed, such as lollipops, gumballs, candy bars, cookies, Cracker Jack, ice cream, etc.).

* In the movie, Shirley talks about wanting to be a pilot. What did you want to be when you were little? (Prompt with examples as needed, such as pilot, fireman, President of the United States, chef, doctor, nurse, teacher, baseball player/professional athlete, musician, actor/actress, dancer, astronaut, police officer, writer, veterinarian, scientist, lawyer, etc.)

(SOMEWHERE) OVER THE RAINBOW

SONG: *"(Somewhere) Over the Rainbow"*
COMPOSERS/WRITERS: *Harold Arlen (music), E.Y. Harburg (lyrics)*
ARTIST(S): *Judy Garland*
YEAR(S) RELEASED: *1939*

ADDITIONAL INFORMATION

Written for *The Wizard of Oz*, this song won an Oscar for "Best Original Song" in 1939. It has been covered by numerous artists and was voted number one on both the "Songs of the Century" list and the American Film Institute's "100 Years…100 Songs" list.

ENGAGED LISTENING

Encourage your loved one to sing along and take a deep breath before the start of each phrase.

MEANINGFUL DISCUSSION

* What actress sang this song in *The Wizard of Oz*? (Judy Garland) What was the character's name? (Dorothy) What was her dog's name? (Toto) Who were the three friends she met along the way? (the Scarecrow, the Tin Man, the Cowardly Lion) Can you name other characters from the movie? (The Wicked Witch of the West, the Munchkins, Glinda the Good Witch, the Wizard, etc.) What color was the brick road they had to follow? (yellow) What shoes did Dorothy find and wear? (ruby red slippers)

* Have you ever seen a rainbow? What are the colors in the rainbow? (red, orange, yellow, green, blue, indigo, violet) When do rainbows appear in the sky? (When the sun comes out while it is raining or right after a rain when the air is still moist.)

* Many people view rainbows as a sign of hope. What do you think? (Discuss the idea of a beautiful rainbow appearing after a storm as it relates to hope after a difficult time in life).

* This song describes a place "somewhere over the rainbow" as a happy, peaceful place free from worries and full of hope. Do you have a special place that can always make you feel peaceful and happy? Where is it?

QUE SERA, SERA (WHATEVER WILL BE, WILL BE)

SONG: *"Que Sera, Sera (Whatever Will Be, Will Be)"*
COMPOSERS/WRITERS: *Ray Evans & Jay Livingston (writers)*
ARTIST(S): *Doris Day*
YEAR(S) RELEASED: *1956*

ADDITIONAL INFORMATION

This song was specifically written for Doris Day to sing in the Alfred Hitchcock movie *The Man Who Knew Too Much*, a 1956 remake of the original 1934 Hitchcock film. It went on to become Doris Day's biggest hit and what some consider to be her signature song. It won the Oscar for "Best Song" in 1956.

ENGAGED LISTENING

Sway side to side with your loved one as you listen and sing along with this song. The chorus is well-known, so encourage your loved one to sing along.

MEANINGFUL DISCUSSION

* At the beginning of the song, a child is asking her mother a question. What question is she asking? (What will I be?/What will the future hold?)

* What is the mother's response? (whatever will be, will be) Do you agree or disagree with this advice given?

* What advice or words of wisdom did your mother give to you when you were young? What advice did you receive from other adults when you were young? Was there any advice you wish you had been given?

* At the end of the song, the child is all grown up and counseling her little one. What advice does she pass on to her child? (whatever will be, will be—the same wisdom her mother gave to her)

* What advice or words of wisdom have you passed on to your children, grandchildren, and/or nieces and nephews? Have you passed on some of the same advice your parents gave to you? Do you think your children, grandchildren, and nieces and nephews will pass that same advice onto their children?

* What advice would you give to a child today?

RING OF FIRE

SONG: *"Ring of Fire"*
COMPOSERS/WRITERS: *June Carter Cash & Merle Kilgore (writers)*
ARTIST(S): *Johnny Cash*
YEAR(S) RELEASED: *1963*

ADDITIONAL INFORMATION

Sources close to Johnny Cash tell conflicting stories not only about the origin of the song, but also the meaning of the term "ring of fire." It is most commonly thought to refer to the process of falling in love. According to Johnny Cash, his wife June Carter Cash wrote the song, but Cash's first wife claimed she watched him write the song and suspected he gave the credit to June Carter because "she needed the money." It is interesting to note that Johnny Cash was inducted into the Country Music Hall of Fame in 1980 and the Rock and Roll Hall of Fame in 1995. He is one of only a few country artists who have received both honors.

ENGAGED LISTENING

This is a great song for encouraging movement. Feel free to use the suggestions below or to mirror/copy how your loved one moves while listening to the song. Keep in mind your loved one will be more likely to move if he or she sees you moving and you verbally encourage him or her to do so.

Suggested movements include the following:

* tap toes with feet together and then with feet alternating
* lift (tap) heels with feet together and then with feet alternating
* alternate between toe taps and heel lifts (taps)
* kick one leg out at a time
* pat hands together on lap and then pat with alternating hands
* move shoulders up and down together and then alternate, one shoulder at a time

MEANINGFUL DISCUSSION

* What does it feel like to fall in love? Is it fiery like the song says, or is it calm and rational? How else does love feel? (Prompt with examples as needed, such as comforting, joyous, warm, peaceful, passionate, secure, disorienting, overwhelming, etc.)

* Have you ever been in love? How long did it last?

* Do you think falling in love is "fiery" in a transformative way or a destructive way? Does it depend on who you fall in love with?

* Where and when did you meet your first love? How old were you? How would you describe your first love?

ROCK AROUND THE CLOCK

SONG: *"Rock Around the Clock"*
COMPOSERS/WRITERS: *Max C. Freedman & James E. Myers (writers)*
ARTIST(S): *Bill Haley & His Comets*
YEAR(S) RELEASED: *1954*

ADDITIONAL INFORMATION

This song is widely considered to be the song that brought rock and roll into mainstream culture world-wide. It reached number one on charts in both the United States and the United Kingdom, and is ranked number 158 on the *Rolling Stone*'s "500 Greatest Songs of All Time" list. It was also the first million-selling single in the United Kingdom. "Rock Around the Clock" was featured under the opening credits of the film *Blackboard Jungle*, intended to represent the types of music popular with the youth in 1955.

ENGAGED LISTENING

Encourage your loved one to move and dance with the rhythm of this song. Suggested movements include: snap fingers, tap toes, kick one leg out at a time, lift shoulders up and down, and do the twist while seated or standing.

MEANINGFUL DISCUSSION

* Have you ever stayed out all night? Why?

* Do you like to dance? Did you ever dance all night?

* This is one of the most famous rock and roll songs of all time. Are you a fan of rock and roll music? Do you remember when rock and roll music first became popular? What do you remember about that time?

(GET YOUR KICKS ON) ROUTE 66

SONG: *"(Get Your Kicks On) Route 66"*
COMPOSERS/WRITERS: *Bobby Troup (writer)*
ARTIST(S): *Nat King Cole, Bing Crosby & The Andrews Sisters*
YEAR(S) RELEASED: *1946*

ADDITIONAL INFORMATION

Bobby Troup wrote this song while on a cross-country drive with his wife from Pennsylvania to California. It lists many of the major stops along U.S. Route 66, but leaves out mention of Kansas entirely. The song has been recorded by many artists, including Perry Como, the Rolling Stones, Natalie Cole, and, most famously, Nat King Cole.

ENGAGED LISTENING

Encourage your loved one to snap his or her fingers or clap his or her hands along with the beat. Additionally, encourage your loved one to tap his or her toes and kick with alternating legs as you listen together. If you have access to the Internet, search for pictures of the different locations mentioned in the song and of Route 66 itself to aid in the meaningful discussion below.

MEANINGFUL DISCUSSION

* Have you ever taken a road trip? Where did your trip start? What was your final destination? What stops did you make along the way? Who did you travel with? Did you enjoy the trip? What was the purpose for the trip?

* Route 66 is over 2,400 miles long. What is the longest road trip you've ever taken? How long did it take you to get where you were going?

* Of the different places mentioned in the song, which have you visited? (Places mentioned in the song include: Chicago, Illinois; Los Angeles, California; St. Louis, Missouri; Joplin, Missouri; Oklahoma City, Oklahoma; Amarillo, Texas; Gallup, New Mexico; Flagstaff, Arizona; Winona, Arizona; Kingman, Arizona; Barstow, California; San Bernardino, California) What do you remember about them?

* When traveling, do you prefer to drive or fly straight to your destination, or sight-see along the way?

* Have you ever driven any part of Route 66? If so, what do you remember about it?

SCHOOL DAYS
(WHEN WE WERE A COUPLE OF KIDS)

SONG: *"School Days (When We Were A Couple of Kids)"*
COMPOSERS/WRITERS: *Gus Edwards & Will Cobb (writers)*
ARTIST(S): *Byron Harlon, Tiny Tim*
YEAR(S) RELEASED: *1907*

ADDITIONAL INFORMATION

The song "School Days" was originally written and recorded in 1907. The song is from the point of view of someone looking back and thinking fondly of his or her school days. This should not be confused with another song titled "School Days" by Chuck Berry that came out in 1957. When searching for the song be sure to include the date, 1907, to find the correct version.

ENGAGED LISTENING

Encourage your loved one to sway from side to side while listening to this song.

MEANINGFUL DISCUSSION

* What academic subjects does the singer mention in the song? (reading, writing, and arithmetic) Did you have any favorite subjects in school? If so, which ones?

* The singer mentions "you wrote on my slate." Did you ever have a slate or individual chalk board at your desk? How did you take notes when you were going to school? Do they still use slates today? (Yes! Children use electronic tablets and iPads in school over 100 years later!)

* Have you ever heard of a hickory stick like the song mentions? (Teachers used to go out and get a switch or hickory stick and use it for discipline in the classroom.) Were you ever disciplined in class? If so, for what? How were students disciplined when you went to school?

* What else do you remember about your time in school? Did you enjoy going to school? What did you like best about school?

* This song also mentions a young love. Did you ever have a crush on a schoolmate? What can you tell me about him or her?

SENTIMENTAL JOURNEY

SONG: *"Sentimental Journey"*
COMPOSERS/WRITERS: *Les Brown & Ben Homer (music), Bud Green (lyrics)*
ARTIST(S): *Doris Day*
YEAR(S) RELEASED: *1945*

ADDITIONAL INFORMATION

In 1945, "Sentimental Journey" became Doris Day's first number one hit. This song resonated with many Americans who were welcoming soldiers home from World War II.

ENGAGED LISTENING

Gently sway side to side with your loved one while you both tap your toes along with the rhythm of this song.

MEANINGFUL DISCUSSION

* Tell me about a favorite trip that you took! Where did you go? What made this trip or destination so special?

* Did you ever long to take a journey somewhere? If so, where? Did you eventually get to travel there?

* Where did you grow up? Did you move around a lot or stay in one place? Where have you lived?

* Tell me about your home. What made your home special?

* What are some good things about the home you have now? What things make where you live now feel like home? (Prompt with examples as needed, such as friends, family, not having to cook, own room with own decorations, fun activities, etc.)

SHAKE, RATTLE AND ROLL

SONG: *"Shake, Rattle and Roll"*
COMPOSERS/WRITERS: *Jesse Stone, using the name of Charles Calhoun (writer)*
ARTIST(S): *Joe Turner, Bill Haley & His Comets*
YEAR(S) RELEASED: *1954*

ADDITIONAL INFORMATION

In 1954, Jesse Stone wrote the song "Shake, Rattle and Roll" for Big Joe Turner, who did most of his recording while on the road. The phrase "shake, rattle and roll" was popular during Stone's weekly poker games, which was likely the inspiration for the title. Bill Haley & His Comets recorded a popular version of the song in 1954, which reached number seven on the *Billboard* Pop chart. Other notable recordings include Patsy Cline, Elvis Presley, the Beatles, and Huey Lewis and the News.

ENGAGED LISTENING

Prompt your loved one to dance along with you while you listen together. Suggested movements include: tap toes, lift heels, clap hands, roll both arms in front, and shake hands at the wrists.

MEANINGFUL DISCUSSION

* Have you ever used the phrase "shake, rattle and roll"? What do you think the phrase means?
* Do you enjoy the style/rhythm/energy of rock and roll music? Why or why not? What are some of your favorite rock and roll songs?
* Did you ever go to a dance hall or attend a sock hop? What do you remember about these events? What did you wear? Do you prefer dancing to fast or to slow songs?

SHE'LL BE COMING 'ROUND THE MOUNTAIN

SONG: *"She'll Be Coming 'Round the Mountain"*
COMPOSERS/WRITERS: *Traditional/Unknown*
ARTIST(S): *Josh Abbott, Pete Seeger*
YEAR(S) RELEASED: *Traditional/Unknown*

ADDITIONAL INFORMATION

"She'll be Coming 'Round the Mountain" is a traditional American folk song that gained popularity in the late 1800s. Its origins are unknown, but it is believed to have been derived from a spiritual titled "When the Chariot Comes," which is about the second coming of Christ.

ENGAGED LISTENING

Encourage your loved one to move along with this lively and well-known song. Prompt him or her to complete a different movement with each verse. Suggested movements might include the following: tap toes, tap heels, march in place, pat knees, clap hands, kick, and raise and lower the shoulders. You can prompt your loved one to complete movements moving both the left and right sides together or alternating between the right and left sides. Because this song is so well-known, sing along together as you listen and move.

MEANINGFUL DISCUSSION

* Have you ever looked forward to the visit of a friend or family member? What were some things you did to prepare for their arrival? (Prompt with examples as needed, such as clean and tidy the house, cook a special meal, extra grocery shopping, putting clean sheets on the guest bed, planning fun outings or activities, etc.)

* Do (did) you enjoy hosting guests in your home? Why or why not? Do (did) you enjoy being a guest in someone else's home? Why or why not?

* What are (were) some of your favorite meals to prepare when you entertain(ed) guests?

* Did you ever travel far to stay with friends or family? Where did you go? What did you enjoy during your visit? Would you rather have family and friends come see you or would you rather travel to see them? When you travelled to see family, did you prefer to stay in their home or in a hotel nearby?

SHINE ON, HARVEST MOON

SONG: *"Shine on, Harvest Moon"*
COMPOSERS/WRITERS: *Nora Bayes-Norworth (music), Jack Norworth (lyrics)*
ARTIST(S): *Ada Jones & Billy Murray, Bing Crosby & Rosemary Clooney*
YEAR(S) RELEASED: *1908*

ADDITIONAL INFORMATION

Nora Bayes was a famous performer and the wife of Jack Norworth when this song, originally in the Ziegfeld Follies, became popular. The Ziegfeld Follies started out in 1907 as a live variety of theatre productions that combined both the New York styles of Broadway and Vaudeville. These productions were performed until 1931 and also became a radio show titled *The Ziegfeld Follies of the Air.*

ENGAGED LISTENING

Encourage your loved one to move his or her shoulders up and down with this song and then sway side to side. Move both shoulders together first, then alternate between the right and left side.

MEANINGFUL DISCUSSION

* What is a "harvest moon"? (A harvest moon is a full moon during the harvest season. It is called a "harvest moon" because the farmers would extend their workday and harvest their crops by moonlight.)

* Why is the singer excited about the harvest moon? (He is enjoying a romantic date with "his gal" and knows it will soon be too cold for romantic dates outside!)

* Do you think moonlight is romantic? If so, what makes moonlight so romantic? Did you ever go on a date by moonlight? Tell me about it!

* Neil Armstrong was the first person to walk on the moon on July 20, 1969. What was it like when you heard the news? Did you get to watch or listen to the broadcast of the moon landing? Do you recall the quote "That's one small step for man, one giant leap for mankind"?

SIDE BY SIDE

SONG: *"Side by Side"*
COMPOSERS/WRITERS: *Harry M. Woods (writer)*
ARTIST(S): *Cliff "Ukulele Ike" Edwards, Nick Lucas*
YEAR(S) RELEASED: *1927*

ADDITIONAL INFORMATION

Harry Woods composed "Side by Side" as well as several other 1920s standards using a piano, despite only having fingers on his right hand. First written and released in 1927, "Side by Side" has been recorded by numerous famous artists including Kay Starr, The Duke Ellington Orchestra, Brenda Lee, Bill Haley & His Comets, and Dean Martin.

ENGAGED LISTENING

Sit side by side with your loved one and encourage him or her to sway side to side with you as you listen to this song together and emphasize swaying whenever the lyrics "side by side" are sung. You can also encourage your loved one to tilt his or her head from side to side and wave hands with open palms to the beat as you move to the music.

MEANINGFUL DISCUSSION

* What is this song about? (A good friend/sweetheart who is your partner for traveling though life!)

* Who is someone that has helped you travel through the good and the bad times of life? (Prompt with examples as needed, such as a husband/wife, a parent, a best friend, a sibling, an aunt, an uncle, or another family member.) What makes that person such a good person to have by your side? (Prompt with examples as needed, such as loyal, honest, caring, encouraging, always there for you, trustworthy, funny, creative, supportive, etc.)

* Is it easier to weather the hard times of life if someone is there to help "share the load?" Who is someone who is there for you now? What makes him or her special? Are you thankful to have someone to "share the load" with you instead of having to handle it on your own?

* What are/were some of the biggest challenges you have faced in your life? Who or what helped get you through them? How did those challenges help you grow/change as a person?

SINGIN' IN THE RAIN

SONG: *"Singin' in the Rain"*
COMPOSERS/WRITERS: *Nacio Herb Brown (music), Arthur Freed (lyrics)*
ARTIST(S): *Gene Kelly*
YEAR(S) RELEASED: *Originally released in 1929; made famous in the 1952 film* Singin' in the Rain

ADDITIONAL INFORMATION

This song was inspired after Author Freed observed a gentleman drenched in the rain and dancing past his business in 1929. The film *Singin' in the Rain* is a musical comedy that is set in 1927 when actors were transitioning from silent films to talkies. The film starred Gene Kelly, Debbie Reynolds, and Donald O'Connor. It was reported that Gene Kelly was sick with a high fever during the filming of this iconic song and dance scene. "Singin' in the Rain" is the number three song on the American Film Institute's "100 Years…100 Songs" list.

ENGAGED LISTENING

Encourage your loved one to tap his or her toes and heels along with this song. If you are able to connect to the Internet, look up the video of Gene Kelly's performance of the title song. Most will remember his famous dancing number and enjoy watching the scene. You can also mention how impressive his performance was under the circumstances (of his high fever during filming).

MEANINGFUL DISCUSSION

* What is this song about? (singing and dancing in the rain) The singer seems rather happy. Do you think the song is about being happy despite less than ideal circumstances? What are some things that can make you feel happy, even when it's raining or your day is not going so well?

* Why is the singer so happy, even though he is out in the rain? (the sun's in his heart, he is "ready for love") What are some things that can always make you feel like the sun's in your heart?

* Do you enjoy being in the rain? Why or why not? Have you ever played in the rain/jumped in puddles?

* Have you ever been caught in the rain without an umbrella? What do you remember about it?

SIXTEEN TONS

SONG: *"Sixteen Tons"*
COMPOSERS/WRITERS: *Merle Travis (writer & 1947 artist)*
ARTIST(S): *Tennessee Ernie Ford*
YEAR(S) RELEASED: *1947, 1955*

ADDITIONAL INFORMATION

Merle Travis based "Sixteen Tons" on his father, who was a coal miner and used to say, "another day older and deeper in debt." Travis was the first artist to record this song in 1947. In 1955, Tennessee Ernie Ford recorded "Sixteen Tons" and it became a huge hit. Ford shared that he was drawn to this song because his grandfather and uncle were coal miners, like Travis's father. George Davis, a country artist, claims to be the original artist and to have written "Sixteen Tons" in the 1930s with slightly different lyrics, however there is no significant evidence that this is true. Additional notable recordings include Johnny Cash, the Platters, and the Weavers.

ENGAGED LISTENING

While listening to this song, encourage your loved one to move with you. For each chorus, pat your hands on your lap. Complete the following movements during the verses:

* 1st verse—tap toes up and down (together or one foot at a time)
* 2nd verse—lift heels up and down (together or one foot at a time)
* 3rd verse—make a fist and punch arms in front of you one at a time
* 4th verse—lift shoulders up and down (together or one at a time)

MEANINGFUL DISCUSSION

* Did you or anyone you know work as a coal miner? If so, who? This is a particularly challenging job; do you think the singer was able to convey that in the song?

* What was the most challenging job you ever held? What made it challenging? Did you enjoy the job?

SUMMERTIME

SONG: *"Summertime"*

COMPOSERS/WRITERS: *George & Ira Gershwin (music), DuBose Heyward (lyrics)*

ARTIST(S): *Louis Armstrong & Ella Fitzgerald*

YEAR(S) RELEASED: *1935*

ADDITIONAL INFORMATION

"Summertime" was composed by George and Ira Gershwin for the opera *Porgy and Bess*. It is one of the most covered songs in the history of recorded music, and versions by several artists have charted on the United States pop charts including renditions by Billie Holiday, Louis Armstrong and Ella Fitzgerald, Sam Cooke, Billy Stewart, and Janis Joplin. "Summertime" ranked number 52 on the American Film Institute's "100 Years…100 Songs" list.

ENGAGED LISTENING

Encourage your loved one to sway from side to side and snap his or her fingers along with the music.

MEANINGFUL DISCUSSION

* When you think of summertime, what comes to mind? (Prompt with examples as needed, such as warm weather, longer days, no school, camp, swimming, vacation, traveling, etc.)

* What is your favorite season? What do you like about it?

* When you were younger, how did you spend your summer vacation? Did you look forward to the break from school, or did you prefer to be in class?

* Do you think the "livin' is easy" and life moves at a more relaxed pace during the summer? What are some of your favorite ways to relax on a summer's day? (Prompt with suggestions as needed, such as take a walk, sit and sip some tea or lemonade, take a vacation, enjoy a picnic, relax by the pool, fish, sit by the ocean, etc.)

SUMMERTIME BLUES

SONG: *"Summertime Blues"*
COMPOSERS/WRITERS: *Eddie Cochran & Jerry Capehart (writers)*
ARTIST(S): *Eddie Cochran*
YEAR(S) RELEASED: *1958*

ADDITIONAL INFORMATION

While the original version of "Summertime Blues" only peaked at number eight on the *Billboard* Hot 100 chart, it has been widely recognized as a rock and roll standard. It appears as number 73 on *Rolling Stone*'s "500 Greatest Songs of All Time" list, as well as on the Rock and Roll Hall of Fame Museum list of "The Songs That Shaped Rock and Roll." It has been covered by numerous artists, including Olivia Newton-John, the Rolling Stones, and the Beach Boys.

ENGAGED LISTENING

This song has a distinctive, rhythmic guitar beat at the start of each verse. Prompt your loved one to join you in clapping along to this pattern. Encourage him or her to dance along throughout the song.

MEANINGFUL DISCUSSION

- The singer of this song mentions several things he doesn't get to do that cause "the summertime blues." Can you name them? (No date because he has to work late, no car because he called in sick to work, no vacation because he's "too young to vote.")

- For you, is summer a time for the blues, like in the song, or is it a time for happiness? Why do you feel this way? What sorts of things contribute to this feeling?

- Did you ever work a summer job? What was it? Did you enjoy it? Why or why not? Was it only for the summer, or did it continue year-round?

SUNRISE, SUNSET

SONG: *"Sunrise, Sunset"*
COMPOSERS/WRITERS: *Jerry Bock (music), Sheldon Harnick (lyrics)*
ARTIST(S): *Zero Mostel & Maria Karnilova, Topol, & Norma Crane*
YEAR(S) RELEASED: *1964*

ADDITIONAL INFORMATION

"Sunrise, Sunset" was written for the Broadway musical *Fiddler on the Roof*, and is performed during the wedding of the main character's eldest daughter. It is a duet sung by two parents who express their disbelief that their children have grown up so fast. *Fiddler on the Roof* was nominated for ten Tony awards and won nine of them. It held the record for the longest-running Broadway show (ten years) until Grease came along. It was adapted into a film in 1971.

ENGAGED LISTENING

Hold your loved one's hands and gently sway back and forth to the song, raising and lowering his or her arms during the lyrics "sunrise, sunset."

MEANINGFUL DISCUSSION

* Do you have any children? What was it like watching them grow into adults? If you do not have children, was there someone you cared for and/or watched grow up? If so, who was it?

* Are you proud of the adults your children grew into? What makes you so proud of them?

* The singer asks, "What words of wisdom can I give them?" What are some words of wisdom you have passed on to your own children? Did they take your advice? If you do not have children, what are some words of wisdom you think I should know and live by?

* In the musical *Fiddler on the Roof*, this song is sung during the wedding of Tevye's eldest daughter. Did you have a special song played at your wedding? What was it? Why did you choose it?

SUNSHINE ON MY SHOULDERS

SONG: *"Sunshine on My Shoulders"*
COMPOSERS/WRITERS: *John Denver (writer)*
ARTIST(S): *John Denver*
YEAR(S) RELEASED: *1971*

ADDITIONAL INFORMATION

"Sunshine on My Shoulders" was first released on John Denver's album *Poems, Prayers and Promises* in 1971. During an interview about the song, Denver said, "I was so down I wanted to write a feeling-blue song, this is what came out." He re-released the song on his *Greatest Hits* album in 1973. The album sold more than ten million copies worldwide, and the song became his first number one hit on the *Billboard* Hot 100 chart in 1974.

ENGAGED LISTENING

Encourage your loved one to take deep relaxing breaths as he or she listens to this song.

MEANINGFUL DISCUSSION

* What does the singer say makes him happy? (sunshine on his shoulders) What are some things that make you happy?

* What does the singer say makes him cry? (sunshine in his eyes) What are some things that can make you cry, either happy or sad tears?

* Denver describes sunshine as something that can both make him happy and make him cry, what are some things that can both make you happy and make you cry?

* What does the singer say looks so lovely? (sunshine on the water) What are some things in nature that you find especially lovely?

* When the singer says, "Sunshine almost always makes me high," what do you think he means by this? (makes him energized, elated, lighthearted, etc.) How does sunshine make you feel? What are some other things that make you feel energized?

* Denver talks about making a wish for sunshine for someone he cares about. Who is someone you would make a wish for sunshine for? What does it mean to "wish for sunshine" for someone? (You are wishing him or her happiness.)

SURFIN' SAFARI

SONG: *"Surfin' Safari"*
COMPOSERS/WRITERS: *Brian Wilson & Mike Love (writers)*
ARTIST(S): *The Beach Boys*
YEAR(S) RELEASED: *1962*

ADDITIONAL INFORMATION

"Surfin' Safari" was the Beach Boys' first major hit and the song itself was entirely self-produced. The Beach Boys were comprised of five members; three brothers—Brian Wilson, Carl Wilson, and Dennis Wilson, their cousin, Mike Love, and a former classmate, Al Jardine. Their music is associated with summertime and often includes the topics of surfing, cars, girls, and love. The Beach Boys were one of several groups in California who made "surfer rock" or "surf music" popular.

ENGAGED LISTENING

Encourage your loved one to dance along with you, moving your arms in a swimming motion and doing "the twist." If you have access to the Internet, find pictures of the beach as well as ocean waves and surfers to aid in the discussion below.

MEANINGFUL DISCUSSION

* What do you think of when you listen to this song? (Prompt with suggestions as needed, such as summertime, having fun, vacation, going to the beach, swimming, surfing, dancing, being outdoors, etc.)

* Have you ever taken a vacation or a trip to the beach? Where did you go? Who did you go with?

* If you've been to the beach, did you have fun? What activities did you enjoy while you were there? (Prompt with examples as needed, such as swimming, sunbathing, having a picnic, building a sandcastle, looking for shells, feeding the sea gulls, taking a walk, wading, people watching, surfing, sailing, fishing, playing volleyball, etc.)

* Do you have a favorite vacation spot? What makes this place your favorite vacation spot? Did your family have any vacation traditions?

* Have you ever been surfing? Were you able to stand up on the board before wiping out? Have you ever seen surfers in the ocean? Do you think surfing looks like fun?

TAKE ME HOME, COUNTRY ROADS

SONG: *"Take Me Home, Country Roads"*
COMPOSERS/WRITERS: *Bill Danoff, Tally Nivert, & John Denver (writers)*
ARTIST(S): *John Denver*
YEAR(S) RELEASED: *1971*

ADDITIONAL INFORMATION

"Take Me Home, Country Roads" is considered John Denver's signature song. This song became the official state anthem of West Virginia in 2014, and is considered an iconic song of the state, despite the fact that most of the lyrics refer to places more commonly associated with Virginia than West Virginia. None of the three authors of the song had ever been to West Virginia when the song was written, basing the lyrics instead on a drive through Maryland and the contents of postcards from a friend in West Virginia.

ENGAGED LISTENING

While listening, sing along with the chorus of the song and encourage your loved one to sing with you. If you have access to the Internet, search for pictures of the Blue Ridge Mountains, Shenandoah River, and the landscapes of West Virginia. Share these pictures with your loved one as you are listening to the song and to help aid in the discussion below.

MEANINGFUL DISCUSSION

* Can you name some of the landscapes and places that John Denver sings about? (West Virginia, Blue Ridge Mountains, Shenandoah River, country roads, blue water, etc.)

* Have you ever been to West Virginia? What do you remember about it? Was it a destination, or were you just passing through?

* The song talks about going "home, to a place I belong." Where do you consider your home? Is it where you were born? Where you grew up? Where you live now? Is it where your family and friends reside? Is it possible to have more than one place where you belong? What makes your home special?

* How would you describe the landscape of your home? (Prompt with examples as needed, such as cold and snowy, hot and dry, windy, full of forests, mountainous, a big city, on the coast, etc.)

TAKE ME OUT TO THE BALLGAME

SONG: *"Take Me Out to the Ballgame"*
COMPOSERS/WRITERS: *Jack Norworth (lyrics), Albert Von Tilzer (music)*
ARTIST(S): *Gene Kelly, The Wurlitzer Pipe Organ (instrumental)*
YEAR(S) RELEASED: *1908*

ADDITIONAL INFORMATION

Neither Jack Norworth nor Albert Von Tilzer had ever been to a baseball game at the time they wrote this song. Norworth wrote the lyrics after being inspired by a subway poster. This song is typically sung during the seventh inning stretch and everyone in the ball park is encouraged to stand up and sing along.

ENGAGED LISTENING

Try holding your loved one's hands and gently swaying side to side with the beat. If singing along, encourage your loved one to replace the words "home team" with the name of his or her favorite team. Alternatively, encourage your loved one to gesture like an umpire during "one, two, three strikes you're out," by doing the motions with them, holding fingers up to count before giving the gesture for "out."

MEANINGFUL DISCUSSION

* Have you ever been to a baseball game? Did you enjoy it? Who did you go with? What team(s) did you watch?

* What sort of foods are popular at baseball games? (Prompt with examples as needed, such as hot dogs, soda pop, beer, peanuts, Cracker Jack, popcorn, ice cream, etc.)

* Did you ever play baseball when you were younger, for fun or on an official team? What position did you play? What different positions are there on a baseball team? (Prompt with examples as needed, such as pitcher, catcher, batter, short stop, outfielder, first, second, third baseman, etc.) Did you ever hit a home run?

* Do you like to watch baseball on television? Are you following or rooting for any teams this year?

* Did you ever enjoy collecting baseball cards?

TENNESSEE WALTZ

SONG: *"Tennessee Waltz"*
COMPOSERS/WRITERS: *Pee Wee King (music), Redd Stewart (lyrics)*
ARTIST(S): *Patti Page*
YEAR(S) RELEASED: *1948 (original), 1950 (Patti Page version)*

ADDITIONAL INFORMATION

"Tennessee Waltz" has been recorded by numerous artists, most famously Patti Page, whose recording sold over ten million copies. It has appeared on the *Billboard* charts several times and was number one on the Pop, R&B, and Country charts, as well as charting in multiple countries across the globe. "Tennessee Waltz" was also the last song to sell a million copies of sheet music. The song is the fourth official song of the state of Tennessee.

ENGAGED LISTENING

Hold your loved one's hands and gently sway side to side on the beat. Encourage him or her to step from side to side as well.

MEANINGFUL DISCUSSION

* Do you like to waltz? What other types of dances do you enjoy? (Prompt with examples as needed, such as foxtrot, tango, jitterbug, Charleston, two step, ballroom, square dancing, country line dancing, swing, etc.)

* Have you ever stolen someone else's sweetheart, like in the song? Did anyone ever steal or try to steal your sweetheart?

* Did you ever have a relationship that ended and was really hard to get over? What helped to heal your heart?

* Have you ever been to Tennessee? What did you remember about it? What are some famous places in Tennessee? (Prompt with examples as needed, such as Nashville, Dollywood, Grand Ol' Opry, Memphis, Graceland (the home of Elvis), Great Smokey Mountains, Pigeon Forge, etc.)

THAT'LL BE THE DAY

SONG: *"That'll Be the Day"*
COMPOSERS/WRITERS: *Jerry Allison, Buddy Holly, Norman Petty (writers)*
ARTIST(S): *Buddy Holly & the Crickets*
YEAR(S) RELEASED: *1957*

ADDITIONAL INFORMATION

"That'll Be the Day," number 39 on *Rolling Stone*'s "500 Greatest Songs of All Time" list, was inspired by the line ("that'll be the day") that John Wayne repeats frequently in the movie *The Searchers*. While Norman Petty is frequently credited as a writer, sources say that although he produced the song, he did not contribute to its actual composition. Buddy Holly, famous as a singer/songwriter, died tragically in a plane crash when he was just 22 years old.

ENGAGED LISTENING

Encourage your loved one to sway side to side and move his or her shoulders with you as you listen to this song together.

MEANINGFUL DISCUSSION

- What do you think this song is about? (love and the idea that it will last)
- The phrase "that'll be the day" repeats over and over. What does it mean? ("That'll be the day" suggests a day that will never come or something that will never happen. In this context, it is suggested in a light-hearted manner that this relationship will never come to an end.)
- Have you ever used the phrase "that'll be the day" to suggest that you think something will never happen? Have you ever been convinced something would never happen, and then it did? What was it? How did you react?

THEME FROM NEW YORK, NEW YORK

SONG: *"Theme from* New York, New York*"*
COMPOSERS/WRITERS: *Fred Ebb (lyrics), John Kander (music)*
ARTIST(S): *Liza Minnelli, Frank Sinatra*
YEAR(S) RELEASED: *1977, 1979, 1993*

ADDITIONAL INFORMATION

"Theme from *New York, New York*," commonly known as "New York, New York," was written for the 1977 Martin Scorsese movie of the same name. Liza Minnelli sang the song in the movie, where she starred opposite Robert De Niro. A year later, in 1978, Frank Sinatra began performing the song in concert, and shortly thereafter, it became one of his signature songs. In 1985, the song was proclaimed as the official anthem of New York City, although it was never actually installed as such. It is played at every home game of the New York Yankees, as well as during the Macy's Thanksgiving Day Parade, and after "Auld Lang Syne" during the New Year's celebration in Times Square.

ENGAGED LISTENING

While listening to the song, alternate between snapping your fingers and kicking your feet. Encourage your loved one to do the same. If you have access to the Internet, search for pictures of iconic symbols of New York City (Empire State Building, Brooklyn Bridge, Statue of Liberty, Rockefeller Center, the Chrysler Building, Central Park, Broadway, Times Square, etc.) to aid in the discussion below.

MEANINGFUL DISCUSSION

* Have you ever been to New York City? What do you remember about it? What are some things New York City is famous for? (Prompt with examples as needed, such as the Statue of Liberty, Empire State Building, Times Square, Broadway, Brooklyn Bridge, Rockefeller Center, shopping, pizza, etc.) If you have the pictures from the engaged listening, ask your loved one to identify iconic New York features.

* The singer talks about leaving small town life to start fresh in the big bustling city of New York. Have you ever lived in a small town? A big city? Which did you prefer and why?

* The song mentions, "If I can make it there, I'll make it anywhere." Did you ever attempt something you were not sure you could accomplish? If so, what was it? How did you feel once you accomplished it? Like the singer, did you feel that once you conquered it, you could take on any challenge?

* The song talks about achieving a lofty dream. What is a dream you had and achieved? (Prompt with examples as needed, such as being a famous actor/singer/performer, etc., visiting all 50 states, climbing a mountain or a specific trail, having a family, getting your "dream" job, writing a book, traveling to a specific state or country, visiting a famous landmark, getting a hole in one, bowling a perfect game, hitting a home run, etc.)

THIS LAND IS YOUR LAND

SONG: *"This Land Is Your Land"*
COMPOSERS/WRITERS: *Woody Guthrie (writer)*
ARTIST(S): *Woody Guthrie*
YEAR(S) RELEASED: *1940 (written), 1944 (recorded), 1951 (released)*

ADDITIONAL INFORMATION

Woody Guthrie wrote this song as a sort of response to the Irving Berlin hit "God Bless America," which he apparently found irritating. His original song included additional verses that were never officially released.

ENGAGED LISTENING

Encourage your loved one to move along with the beat of this song. Encourage him or her to complete movements such as tapping toes, marching in place, patting knees, and clapping. If you have access to the Internet, look up images of the specific locations and landscapes mentioned in the song to aid in the discussion below. Locations and landscapes to view may include New York Island, California, the redwood forest, the Gulf Stream, beaches, mountains, prairies, deserts, rolling hills, flat plains, forests, valleys, etc.)

MEANINGFUL DISCUSSION

* What "land" is this song talking about? (United States of America)

* What locations or sites in America does the song reference? (New York Island, California, redwood forest, Gulf Stream, etc.)

* In what state were you born? In what other states have you lived? What makes this (these) states special and what do (did) you enjoy about living in them? What has been your favorite place to live in America?

* It's amazing how much diversity there is in the American landscape! What kinds of different landscapes do we have? (Prompt with examples as needed, such as beaches, mountains, prairies, deserts, rolling hills, flat plains, forests, valleys, etc.)

* What was your favorite place to visit in America? Why did you enjoy visiting so much? (If your loved one is struggling, offer some suggestions of states, cities, or specific landmarks.)

TIPTOE THROUGH THE TULIPS

SONG: *"Tiptoe Through the Tulips"*
COMPOSERS/WRITERS: *Al Dubin (lyrics), Joe Burke (music)*
ARTIST(S): *Nick Lucas, Tiny Tim*
YEAR(S) RELEASED: *1929 (Nick Lucas), 1968 (Tiny Tim)*

ADDITIONAL INFORMATION

This song was originally written for the musical "talkie" film *Gold Diggers of Broadway* in 1929. Nick Lucas's recording held the number one position on the charts for ten weeks. The song charted at number 5, 11, and 18 as well that year by three other artists. In 1930, the song appeared in the first *Looney Tunes* cartoon short *Sinkin' in the Bathtub*. It was re-released in 1968 by Tiny Tim, whose rendition became known for its high-pitched falsetto vocals and ukulele accompaniment.

ENGAGED LISTENING

Encourage your loved one to tap his or her toes along with the song. Take your loved one's hands and swing them up and down and side to side with the music. If you have access to the Internet, search for pictures of tulips and other flowers to aid in the discussion below.

MEANINGFUL DISCUSSION

* Have you ever taken a walk through a garden or field? Was it your own garden or someone else's garden? Have you ever visited landmark gardens, such as those around a castle or historical estate or botanical gardens in a specific city? If so, where?

* What are your favorite flowers? (Prompt with examples as needed, such as tulips, roses, daisies, daffodils, etc.)

* Do (did) you like to garden? What kind of plants do (did) you like to grow?

* Does a moonlit stroll through a flower garden sound like a romantic date to you?

* Have you ever kissed someone or been kissed in the moonlight? Where? When? Who were you with?

WALKIN' AFTER MIDNIGHT

SONG: *"Walkin' After Midnight"*
COMPOSERS/WRITERS: *Alan Block & Don Hecht (writers)*
ARTIST(S): *Patsy Cline*
YEAR(S) RELEASED: *1957*

ADDITIONAL INFORMATION

"Walkin' After Midnight" was Patsy Cline's first hit song. She first performed it on Arthur Godfrey's *Talent Scouts* television program in 1957. After her television performance, the song became a crossover hit, reaching number two on the *Billboard* Country charts and number 12 on the *Billboard* Pop charts.

ENGAGED LISTENING

Encourage your loved one to move along with the song with the following suggested movements: walk or march in place with the beat, move alternating feet to the side and back to center, or swing arms as if marching.

MEANINGFUL DISCUSSION

* Have you ever been walking late at night? How would you describe being out in the moonlight? (Prompt with examples as needed, such as peaceful, scary, calm, mysterious, quiet, still, etc.)

* The singer says she is walking after midnight searching for her beau. Do you think she is literally looking for him or is she also looking to relive some of the best memories of their relationship?

* The singer talks about a lost love. Have you ever experienced a love that was lost? How did you get through it? Did you meet someone else? Did you have a friend to help you get past it?

* Did (do) you and your sweetheart have any special places that were (are) meaningful to the two of you? Where was (is) it?

* Did you ever visit a special spot just to relive a past memory? Where did you visit? Why was this place so meaningful? Did visiting this place make you happy or sad?

THE WAY YOU LOOK TONIGHT

SONG: *"The Way You Look Tonight"*
COMPOSERS/WRITERS: *Jerome Kern (music), Dorothy Fields (lyrics)*
ARTIST(S): *Fred Astaire, Bing Crosby & Dixie Lee Crosby, Frank Sinatra*
YEAR(S) RELEASED: *1936*

ADDITIONAL INFORMATION

Originally performed by Fred Astaire in the film *Swing Time*, "The Way You Look Tonight" won the 1936 Oscar for "Best Original Song" and is listed as number 43 on the American Film Institute's "100 Years…100 Songs" list as well. The song is considered a jazz standard, and has been covered by many artists, including Ella Fitzgerald, Peggy Lee, Tony Bennett, and Perry Como.

ENGAGED LISTENING

Hold your loved one's hands and help him or her to dance along with the song while seated. If he or she is able, have your loved one stand and dance with you to the music.

MEANINGFUL DISCUSSION

* The singer talks about the little things(s) he loves about his/her sweetheart, like a warm smile, soft cheeks, and a laugh "that wrinkles your nose." What are some of the little things you love(d) about your sweetheart?

* What is something about your sweetheart that caught your eye the first time you saw him or her?

* Tell me a favorite memory (or two or three) of your sweetheart and the times you spent together!

* Who is someone that always brings a smile to your face when you think about him or her? What is it about him or her that makes you smile?

* Do you remember a time when you felt particularly beautiful or handsome? What were you wearing? What was the occasion?

WHAT A FRIEND WE HAVE IN JESUS

SONG: *"What a Friend We Have in Jesus"*
COMPOSERS/WRITERS: *Joseph Scriven (words), Charles Converse (music)*
ARTIST(S): *Various Artists*
YEAR(S) RELEASED: *1855 (text), 1868 (tune), 1886 (published)*

ADDITIONAL INFORMATION

Joseph Scriven wrote the text of this now famous hymn in 1855 to comfort his mother who lived across the sea from him in Ireland. It was originally published anonymously and was not published under Scriven's name until 1886. The tune of this beloved hymn was written in 1868 by Charles Converse.

ENGAGED LISTENING

Encourage your loved one to relax and take deep breaths as you listen to this song together.

MEANINGFUL DISCUSSION

* The song encourages us to take everything to God in prayer. Do you agree with this advice?

* The song says that often we forfeit peace or bear pain needlessly because we forget to take it to God in prayer or do not fully trust Him with our troubles. Do you think this is true?

* Was there a time you struggled to fully trust God with your troubles? Can you tell me about it? Do you think there are times almost everyone struggles with fully trusting in God with challenges and sorrows?

* Do you think that trusting in God means that you will always be happy, or can you still be sad or grieving through a painful time, even if you are trusting God? Is it possible to feel the peace of the Lord in the midst of feeling grief as well? Can you tell me about a time your faith in God remained strong, even while you were sad or struggling?

* Tell me about a time(s) God answered your prayers.

* What are you praying about today? (If you are comfortable, offer to pray with him or her over some of the challenges and praises mentioned.)

WHAT A WONDERFUL WORLD

SONG: *"What a Wonderful World"*
COMPOSERS/WRITERS: *Bob Thiele & George Weiss (writers)*
ARTIST(S): *Louis Armstrong*
YEAR(S) RELEASED: *1967*

ADDITIONAL INFORMATION

When the song "What a Wonderful World" was first released and recorded by Louis Armstrong, it barely made the charts in the United States. It did, however, top the charts in the United Kingdom. Two decades later in 1988, it was featured in the film *Good Morning Vietnam*, starring Robin Williams. Louis Armstrong's recording was re-released and it reached number 32 on the *Billboard* Hot 100 chart.

ENGAGED LISTENING

This song asks us to stop, take in our surroundings, and acknowledge the beauty around us. While this song is playing, encourage your loved one to look out the window at his or her surroundings. If you do not have a window close by, ask your loved one to close his or her eyes and try to imagine the images that are mentioned in the song (green trees, red roses, blue skies, etc.). This activity will help facilitate the discussion below.

MEANINGFUL DISCUSSION

* Encourage your loved one to look out the window or around the room. What do you see? (Prompt with examples as needed, such as buildings, trees, flowers, people, colors, friends, artwork on the walls, decorations, etc.) Is what you see mentioned in the song? (song examples include: green trees, red roses, blue skies, white clouds, colors of the rainbow)

* Have you ever heard the phrase "stop and smell the roses"? What does that phrase mean to you? (One example could be to take time to pause, enjoy life, and appreciate the little things.) Do you think that can apply to this song? What are some ways you can "stop and smell the roses"?

* Do you think it is important to stop and appreciate your surroundings?

* When you think about "a wonderful world," what is that world like? Do we live in it today? Why or why not? What would you change to make this world more wonderful?

WHEN THE SAINTS GO MARCHING IN

SONG: *"When the Saints Go Marching In"*
COMPOSERS/WRITERS: *Traditional/Unknown*
ARTIST(S): *Louis Armstrong & His Orchestra/Various Artists*
YEAR(S) RELEASED: *Traditional (1938 Louis Armstrong Version)*

ADDITIONAL INFORMATION

Considered a traditional hymn or spiritual, the exact origin of "When the Saints Go Marching In" is unknown. The song was first made famous by Louis Armstrong after he recorded it in 1938 and has since been recorded by numerous and varied artists. This song is widely considered the unofficial anthem of the city of New Orleans, the birthplace of jazz. It is also a staple for most Dixieland bands. "When the Saints Go Marching In" has been used in New Orleans and other parts of Louisiana for celebrations, including but not limited to birthdays, weddings, and celebrating someone's life after he or she has passed away.

ENGAGED LISTENING

This ever-popular march is ideal for movement. Encourage your loved one to complete a different movement with each verse and chorus and remember he or she will be more likely to move if you are completing the movements as well. Suggested movements include: tap toes, march in place, kicks, pat knees, clap hands, alternate between patting knees and clapping hands, shrug shoulders.

MEANINGFUL DISCUSSION

* What does "when the saints go marching in" mean? (It refers to people marching into heaven.)

* New Orleans is known as the "birthplace of jazz." Do you enjoy jazz music? What are some of the instruments in a jazz band? (saxophone, trumpet, piano, bass, guitar, trombone, drums, etc.) Do you have any favorite jazz musicians? If not, have you heard of these musicians? (Prompt with suggestions as needed, such as Louis Armstrong, Dizzie Gillespie, Miles Davis, John Coltrane, Duke Ellington, Charlie Parker, Ella Fitzgerald, Count Basie, Billie Holiday, and Ray Charles.)

* How does this song make you feel?

WHEN YOU WISH UPON A STAR

SONG: *"When You Wish Upon a Star"*
COMPOSERS/WRITERS: *Ned Washington & Leigh Harline (writers)*
ARTIST(S): *Cliff Edwards*
YEAR(S) RELEASED: *1940*

ADDITIONAL INFORMATION

This song was originally written for and featured in the 1940 Disney movie *Pinocchio*. Cliff Edwards, the voice of Jiminy Cricket, sang it at the beginning and the end of the movie. "When You Wish Upon a Star" won the 1941 Oscar for "Best Song." It is also interesting to note that this song is used to celebrate Christmastime in Sweden, Denmark, and Norway.

ENGAGED LISTENING

If you have access to the Internet, look up images of stars and the starry sky at night to view with your loved one as you listen to this song.

MEANINGFUL DISCUSSION

* What movie is this song from? (Prompt with hints as needed, such as: It was an animated film by Disney that came out in 1940; It was the story of a wooden puppet; Every time he told a lie, his nose grew longer.)

* What was Pinocchio's wish in the movie? (He wanted to be a real boy.) Did his wish come true? (Yes)

* Have you ever made a wish on a star before? What did you wish for? Did your wish come true?

* What kinds of stars do people wish on? (shooting star/falling star, first star at night)

* See if your loved one can complete the poem: "Starlight, star bright…" (Prompt as needed with the rest of the poem; "first star I see tonight, I wish I may, I wish I might have the wish I wish tonight.")

* If you saw the first star tonight, what would you wish for?

WITH A LITTLE HELP FROM MY FRIENDS

SONG: *"With a Little Help From My Friends"*
COMPOSERS/WRITERS: *John Lennon & Paul McCartney (writers)*
ARTIST(S): *The Beatles, Joe Cocker*
YEAR(S) RELEASED: *1967*

ADDITIONAL INFORMATION

John Lennon and Paul McCartney worked together and wrote the majority of the music the Beatles performed. "With a Little Help From My Friends" is said to be one of the last songs that they composed together. The drummer, Ringo Starr, sang the lead vocals. Although "With a Little Help From My Friends" was not originally released as a single, it continues to be one of their most well-known songs. There have been many covers of this song, but the most popular version is by Joe Cocker in 1968. In 2015, Ringo Starr performed "With a Little Help From My Friends" when he was inducted into The Rock and Roll Hall of Fame.

ENGAGED LISTENING

Encourage your loved one to sway from side to side with you as you listen to this song together.

MEANINGFUL DISCUSSION

* Have you stayed in touch with friends you made while growing up? If so, how? (Prompt with examples as needed, such as talk on the phone, write letters, plan visits to meet up, etc.)

* What are the qualities you look for in a friend? (Prompt with examples as needed, such as trustworthy, caring, loyal, supportive, fun, sharing common interests, etc.)

* The singers talk about how things are a little easier with help from friends. Do you think this is true? Can you think back to a difficult situation where a friend was there for you? How did it feel to have someone on your side? What did your friend do to help and support you?

* The singers mention, "I'm gonna try with a little help from my friends." Was there a time where you didn't want to go through with something but a friend was there to encourage you to complete the task/job? If so, what was it? How did it turn out?

* What is something you can do to help or encourage a friend who is having a difficult time?

* Ask your loved one if there is something you can do to help him or her today.

YAKETY YAK

SONG: *"Yakety Yak"*
COMPOSERS/WRITERS: *Jerry Lieber and Mike Stoller (writers)*
ARTIST(S): *The Coasters*
YEAR(S) RELEASED: *1958*

ADDITIONAL INFORMATION

Jerry Lieber and Mike Stoller were a dynamic songwriting duo who wrote several songs for the Coasters as well as several hits for Elvis Presley including "Hound Dog" and "Jailhouse Rock." When the song "Yakety Yak" was released in 1958, it spent seven weeks in the number one spot on the *Billboard* R&B chart as well as one week in the number one spot on the *Billboard* Hot 100 chart.

ENGAGED LISTENING

Encourage your loved one to move along to the beat of this song. Suggested movements include: tap toes, move from side to side, dance standing and/ or sitting. During the chorus, "yakety yak, don't talk back," encourage your loved one to make a talking motion with his or her hand during "yakety yak" and then wag a finger during "don't talk back."

MEANINGFUL DISCUSSION

* This song mentions all the chores that need to be done before going out on a Friday night to earn some "spending cash." Can you name some of the chores mentioned in the song? (scrub the kitchen floor, clean your room, sweep, do laundry, take out the trash, etc.).

* When you were younger, what chores were you were responsible for? (Prompt with suggestions as needed, such as clean the kitchen or bathroom floor, dust the house, vacuum, mop, cut the grass, rake leaves, laundry, clean your room, take out the garbage, wash the dishes, take care of the pets, etc.) Did you ever give your parents a hard time about having to do chores when you were younger?

* If you have children, did you ask them to do chores around the house? If so, did they ever talk back or give you dirty looks as in the song? How did you handle it?

* What are (were) some of your least favorite household chores? What are (were) the household chores you enjoy(ed) the most?

YELLOW SUBMARINE

SONG: *"Yellow Submarine"*
COMPOSERS/WRITERS: *John Lennon & Paul McCartney (writers)*
ARTIST(S): *The Beatles*
YEAR(S) RELEASED: *1966*

ADDITIONAL INFORMATION

The Beatles were a hit in the United Kingdom but did not become famous in the United States until they performed on *The Ed Sullivan Show* in 1964. When the Beatles recorded "Yellow Submarine," Ringo Starr sang lead vocals and the Beatles asked their friends and the studio crew to sing along on the last chorus.

ENGAGED LISTENING

This song is great for encouraging movement. Encourage your loved one to do the following movements with the song. You can change the movements where you feel it is appropriate or follow the prompts below:

- 1st Verse—Pat hands on lap together first and then alternate right and left
- Chorus—March in place
- 2nd Verse—Kick one leg out at a time (as if you are creating a chorus line)
- Chorus—March in place
- Instrumental/Submarine Sound Effects—Move arms up and down
- 3rd Verse—Move shoulders up and down, first both shoulders together and then alternating right and left
- Chorus—March in place

MEANINGFUL DISCUSSION

- Can you name any of the Beatles? If you are able to connect to the Internet, bring up a picture of the Beatles as your loved one tries to name each one. (John Lennon, Paul McCartney, George Harrison, Ringo Starr)
- Do you enjoy the Beatles' music? Why or why not?
- Did you or anyone you know ever dress like the Beatles? (At the time, this was known as *Beatlemania*, and fans would dress like them and also imitate their haircuts.)
- What is a submarine?
- Have you ever been on a submarine? What was it like? Did you ever want to go on a submarine?

YES SIR, THAT'S MY BABY

SONG: *"Yes Sir, That's My Baby"*
COMPOSERS/WRITERS: *Gus Kahn (lyrics) Walter Donaldson (music)*
ARTIST(S): *Ace Brigode, Eddie Cantor*
YEAR(S) RELEASED: *1925*

ADDITIONAL INFORMATION

The song "Yes Sir, That's My Baby" was popular during the Charleston era and is said to have been inspired by a toy pig. While the writers were visiting Eddie Cantor, his daughter Marjorie showed them her mechanical pig, which moved from side to side while playing two notes. Kahn began thinking of lyrics that followed the rhythm of the toy pig, and soon they had composed this hit song.

ENGAGED LISTENING

If you have access to the Internet, search for a video clip of the Charleston to watch with your loved one. Encourage him or her to imitate the fast movements (kicking legs out side to side, lifting/moving arms out side to side and bringing knees in and out) as you listen to the song. If you do not have access to the Internet, you can still use the movements mentioned above.

MEANINGFUL DISCUSSION

* Have you ever danced the Charleston? Where did you like to go dancing? Did you prefer fast dances like the Charleston, slow dances, or did it depend on your partner?

* When you hear this song, does it make you think of anyone in particular? If so, who?

* The singer is excited to declare his love for "my baby" to everyone. When you've been in a relationship, do you like to keep it more private, or declare it to the world?

YES! WE HAVE NO BANANAS

SONG: *"Yes! We Have No Bananas"*
COMPOSERS/WRITERS: *Frank Silver & Irving Cohn (writers)*
ARTIST(S): *Eddie Cantor, Billy Jones & Orchestra*
YEAR(S) RELEASED: *1922*

ADDITIONAL INFORMATION

According to a popular story, Silver and Cohn stopped for a snack at a grocer's on the way to work in New York City when the grocer told them, "Yes! We have no bananas." Bananas were in short supply at the time due to a blight in Central America. Eddie Cantor's version held the number one spot on *Your Hit Parade* for five consecutive weeks. This song has since been recorded by numerous artists.

ENGAGED LISTENING

While listening with your loved one, encourage him or her to sing the repeating line "Yes! We have no bananas," along with you as it occurs in the song.

MEANINGFUL DISCUSSION

* Do you like to eat bananas? What color is an unripe banana? What color is a ripe banana? What color is an overripe banana? What are some dishes you can make with bananas? (Prompt with examples as needed, such as banana bread, banana pudding, banana cream pie, banana split, banana pancakes, peanut butter and banana sandwiches, etc.)

* What other fruits do you like to eat?

* What are some other foods mentioned in this song? (string beans, onions, cabbages, scallions, fruit, potato, tomato, coconuts, walnuts, doughnuts, nuts, herring) Which of the foods mentioned in the song do you enjoy eating?

* What are some of your favorite foods to eat? (If your loved one is struggling, ask a less open-ended question such as, do you prefer sweet or savory foods? Or suggest a variety of foods and ask them to pick a favorite food from the list.)

* This song almost sounds like a grocery list. Did you do a lot of grocery shopping for your family? Did you enjoy doing the grocery shopping?

* Did you like to cook? What were some of the meals you prepared for your family? What were some of your favorite ingredients to use? (If your loved one is struggling, suggest a variety of popular ingredients such as chicken, potatoes, garlic, onions, spices, herbs, rice, beef, broccoli, beans, etc.)

YOU ARE MY SUNSHINE

SONG: *"You Are My Sunshine"*
COMPOSERS/WRITERS: *Jimmie Davis & Charles Mitchell (presumed writers)*
ARTIST(S): *Jimmie Davis*
YEAR(S) RELEASED: *1939*

ADDITIONAL INFORMATION

Although "You are My Sunshine" is widely considered one of the most famous and popular songs of the 20th century in America, its original authorship and release is unclear. While the song is widely attributed to Jimmie Davis and his guitarist Charles Mitchell, there is controversy surrounding the song's actual origin. Both Bing Crosby's and Gene Autry's 1941 versions were considered hits, and the song has since been recorded by numerous artists over several decades. Davis himself later went on to become the governor of Louisiana. This song became one of Louisiana's state songs.

ENGAGED LISTENING

The chorus of this song is very well-known. Encourage your loved one to sing along with you as you listen to the song together.

MEANINGFUL DISCUSSION

* What does it mean for someone to be your sunshine? (Prompt with suggestions as needed, such as they are central to your life, you can count on them to be there every day, they always make you feel better, they can make you laugh, etc.)

* Who is your sunshine? (Prompt with suggestions as needed, such as a spouse, children, grandchildren, parents, friends, uncles and aunts, nieces and nephews, etc.) What makes this person so special?

* Why do you think this song has remained so popular generation after generation?

* Who is someone you see regularly that always makes you happy?

YOU CAN'T HURRY LOVE

SONG: *"You Can't Hurry Love"*
COMPOSERS/WRITERS: *Brian Holland, Lamont Dozier, Eddie Holland (lyrics and music)*
ARTIST(S): *The Supremes*
YEAR(S) RELEASED: *1966*

ADDITIONAL INFORMATION

"You Can't Hurry Love" was a signature song of the Supremes, and was their seventh number one hit. It reached number one on both the *Billboard* Hot 100 and the *Billboard* Soul chart. Inspired by a 1950s gospel song called "(You Can't Hurry God) He's Right on Time," "You Can't Hurry Love" remains well-known today.

ENGAGED LISTENING

While listening to the song, swing your arms to the left then to the right along with the beat, shrug your shoulders, and tap your toes, encouraging your loved one to do the same.

MEANINGFUL DISCUSSION

* The singer mentions her mother's advice that "you can't hurry love." Do you agree with her? Why or why not?

* Does love come easily, does it require hard work, or is it a combination of both? What does it mean to give and take in a relationship? What happens if a couple doesn't give and take the way the song suggests?

* Have you heard the expression "Good things come to those who wait"? Do you think it applies to love?

* Has someone given you "precious words" or advice? If so what was it? Was it helpful?

* Is it hard to wait for something you want very much? What was something you really wanted but had to wait for? (Prompt with suggestions as needed, such as love, a job or a better job, someone to return from war, starting a family, buying a house, completing an education, etc.) What advice would you give someone who was waiting for something he or she really wanted?

YOUR CHEATIN' HEART

SONG: *"Your Cheatin' Heart"*
COMPOSERS/WRITERS: *Hank Williams (writer)*
ARTIST(S): *Hank Williams*
YEAR(S) RELEASED: *1953*

ADDITIONAL INFORMATION

Hank Williams described his first wife as a "cheatin' heart." He felt that this song was "the best heart song" he ever wrote and it is considered to be a significant standard in country music. Hank Williams recorded "Your Cheatin' Heart" in 1952 and passed away before the song was officially released in early 1953.

ENGAGED LISTENING

While listening to this song, encourage your loved one to tap his or her toes, to move his or her hands and arms from side to side and/or pat hands on his or her lap.

MEANINGFUL DISCUSSION

* The singer talks about a "cheatin' heart." What does that mean to you? (Prompt with suggestions as needed, such as unfaithful, untrustworthy, loving someone else, etc.)

* The singer says "your cheatin' heart will tell on you." Do you think this is true? If someone is not being faithful or true, will it catch up with them?

* Are you a fan of Hank Williams' music? What other songs of his can you recall?

ZIP-A-DEE-DOO-DAH

SONG: *"Zip-A-Dee-Doo-Dah"*
COMPOSERS/WRITERS: *Allie Wrubel (music), Ray Gilbert (lyrics)*
ARTIST(S): *Frank Baskett, Johnny Mercer*
YEAR(S) RELEASED: *1946*

ADDITIONAL INFORMATION

"Zip-A-Dee-Doo-Dah" was first performed by James Baskett in the 1946 Walt Disney live action animated film *Song of the South*. Uncle Remus, played by Baskett, is a former slave who shares folk tales and other stories with the children, including tales about the infamous Brer Rabbit. This song went on to win the Oscar for "Best Song" and is listed as number 47 on the American Film Institute's "100 Years…100 Songs" list.

ENGAGED LISTENING

Encourage your loved one to tap his or her toes and shrug and move his or her shoulders with you as you listen together.

MEANINGFUL DISCUSSION

* The singer mentions "plenty of sunshine heading my way." How do you feel when you see sunshine? Does it give you energy or a wonderful feeling like the singer mentions in the song? Do you prefer to be out in the sun, or do you seek shade when you're outside?

* When you hear the phrase "wonderful feeling, wonderful day," what comes to mind? What can help you have a wonderful day? (Prompt with suggestions as needed, such as sunshine, birds, singing or listening to a song, sharing a smile or a laugh with someone, enjoying your favorite food or drink, seeing a loved one, going to a favorite place, etc.)

* When the song refers to "Mr. Bluebird on my shoulder," it suggests a bluebird as a symbol of happiness. What are some things that make you happy?

NEW YEAR'S EVE/DAY

SONGS TO USE

AULD LANG SYNE *Traditional/Guy Lombardo (recommended artist)*
LET'S START THE NEW YEAR RIGHT *1942 Irving Berlin (writer), Bing Crosby (recommended artist)*
RINGIN' IN A BRAND NEW YEAR *1953 Billy Ward & the Dominoes (artist)*
WHAT ARE YOU DOING NEW YEAR'S EVE? *1947 Frank Loesser (writer),
Ella Fitzgerald (recommended artist)*

ADDITIONAL INFORMATION ABOUT THE HOLIDAY

This holiday celebrates the start of the new year, which, according to the Gregorian calendar, occurs on January 1st. While New Year's Day is the official Federal holiday, most celebrations take place the night before on December 31st, New Year's Eve, when people count down to the start of the new year at midnight.

ENGAGED LISTENING

Encourage your loved one to sing the chorus along with you as you both listen to "Auld Lang Syne." When enjoying "Ringin' in a Brand New Year," tap your toes and sway and shake your shoulders along with the beat and encourage your loved one to do the same. Encourage him or her to gently sway side to side with you as you listen to "Let's Start the New Year Right." Hold his or her hands as you move together to encourage more movement if needed.

MEANINGFUL DISCUSSION

* What are some ways people celebrate New Year's Eve and New Year's Day? When you were younger, what were some of your favorite ways to celebrate the start of the new year? (Prompt with examples as needed, such as parties with friends, drinking, champagne toast (and a kiss!) at midnight, dancing, making resolutions, fireworks, noise-makers, watching the New Year's Day Rose Parade or Rose Bowl, watching the ball drop in New York City on television, eating black eyed peas for good luck, gathering together for a big meal on New Year's Day, etc.)

* Do you have any new year's traditions that you have continued from when you were younger? If so, what are they?

* What are you doing to celebrate the new year this year?

* Did you make any new year's resolutions? If so, what are they?

* Do you know what "auld lang syne" means? (The literal translation is "old long since." It can be more loosely translated as "for the sake of long ago," or "for the sake of old times." Essentially, the song is saying to remember times gone by and, moreso, to remember long-lasting friendships. It is sung at new year's to remind us of our nearest and dearest.) Who are some dear friends or family members you are remembering this New Year's Eve? Are you still in touch?

VALENTINE'S DAY

SONGS TO USE

CAN'T HELP FALLING IN LOVE *1961 Hugo Peretti, Luigi Creatore,*
& George David Weiss (writers), Elvis Presley (artist)

FLY ME TO THE MOON *1954 Bart Howard (writer), Peggy Lee, Frank Sinatra (recommended artists)*

LET ME CALL YOU SWEETHEART *1910 Leo Friedman (music), Beth Slater Whitson (lyrics),*
The Peerless Quartet, Bing Crosby (recommended artists)

UNCHAINED MELODY *1955 Alex North (music), Hy Zaret (lyrics), The Righteous Brothers (recommended artist)*

ADDITIONAL INFORMATION ABOUT THE HOLIDAY

The exact origins of Valentine's Day are uncertain. The day is often thought to commemorate the death of Saint Valentine, a Christian martyr who was killed for performing secret marriages against the decree of Emperor Claudius II, who preferred his soldiers be single. Another possible origin is the Roman Lupercalia Festival (of fertility), which was traditionally held on February 15th. Regardless of its origins, the celebration of Valentine's Day began in the 17th century. During the 18th century, the exchange of notes and small tokens of affection between friends and sweethearts became common.

ENGAGED LISTENING

When listening to "Let Me Call You Sweetheart," encourage your loved one to sing along with you. Prompt him or her to gently sway side to side with you as you listen to "Can't Help Falling in Love" together. Encourage your loved one to kick with alternating legs as you listen to "Fly Me to the Moon." Take deep, slow breaths as you listen together to "Unchained Melody."

MEANINGFUL DISCUSSION

* What do we celebrate on Valentine's Day? (love, friendship)

* What are some ways of celebrating Valentine's Day? (Prompt with examples as needed, such as parties, pink, red, and white decorations, chocolates, flowers, sending and receiving cards and valentines, making valentines, dancing, music, going out to dinner, etc.)

* Tell me about your valentine! Did you marry him or her? If so, how long were you married? What made your sweetheart special? (Prompt with examples as needed, such as funny, good looking, smart, caring, a good dancer, kind, took care of you, etc.) What activities do (did) you like to share?

* Would you describe your sweetheart as "romantic"? What are (were) some ways he or she shows(ed) you how much you are loved?

* How do you show your sweetheart, friends, and family that you care about them? What is something people can do to show you that they care?

ST. PATRICK'S DAY

SONGS TO USE

MY WILD IRISH ROSE *1899 Chauncey Olcott (writer & artist),*
The Mills Brothers (recommended artist)

TOO-RA-LOO-RA-LOO-RAL (THAT'S AN IRISH LULLABY) *1913/1914,*
James Royce Shannon (composer), Chauncey Olcott, Mitch Miller (recommended artists)

WHEN IRISH EYES ARE SMILING *1912/1913 George Graf Junior & Chauncey Olcott (lyrics), Ernest R. Ball*
(music), Chauncey Olcott, Bing Crosby (recommended artists)

WHISKEY IN THE JAR *Unknown/Mid 17th century, The Dubliners (recommended artist)*

ADDITIONAL INFORMATION ABOUT THE HOLIDAY

St. Patrick's Day was first celebrated on March 17, 1631 (the day St. Patrick is said to have died). The holiday originated as a religious feast day to honor Patrick, the patron saint of Ireland. He is credited with bringing Christianity to the country. St. Patrick's Day also celebrates Irish heritage and culture. Today, the holiday is celebrated around the world. Its traditions include attending festivals and parades, listening to bag pipes and Irish drumming, Irish step dancing, the wearing of the green, decorating with shamrocks and the colors of the Irish flag (green, white and orange), eating corned beef and cabbage, and drinking Irish whiskey and beer. There is a common misconception that shamrocks and four leaf clovers are the same, however this is not the case. Shamrocks are a type of clover that grow in the winter and have three leaves, not four like the rare and lucky "four leaf clover." St. Patrick is said to have used the shamrock to represent the "Holy Trinity of the Father, the Son, and the Holy Spirit," whereas the four-leaf clover represents "faith, hope, love, and luck."

ENGAGED LISTENING

If you have access to the Internet, find pictures of Ireland including the country-side, beaches, castles, the Cliffs of Moher, the Ring of Kerry, St Patrick's Cathedral, Blarney Stone, etc. to aid the discussion below.

MEANINGFUL DISCUSSION

* What comes to mind when you think of St. Patrick's Day? What are some ways you can celebrate? (Prompt with examples as needed, such as eating corned beef and cabbage, drinking Irish whiskey and beer, dressing in green, decorating with shamrocks, singing Irish folk songs, festivals, parades, etc.)

* Have you ever traveled to Ireland? If so, what do you recall about your trip? If not, what do you think of when you think of Ireland? (Look at the pictures from the engaged listening and talk about them together.)

* It is common to give a traditional Irish toast when celebrating in a group. Have you ever given a toast before? Here is one Irish toast we can share together, "May your blessings outnumber the shamrocks that grow, and may trouble avoid you wherever you go."

PASSOVER (PESACH)

SONGS TO USE

ADIR HU (HE IS MIGHTY) *Traditional/Various Artists*
DAHYENU (IT WOULD HAVE BEEN ENOUGH FOR US) *Traditional/Various Artists*
EILYAHU HANAVI (ELIJAH, THE PROPHET) *Traditional/Various Artists*

ADDITIONAL INFORMATION ABOUT THE HOLIDAY

Passover (Pesach) is the Jewish holiday celebrated each year over the course of eight days to remember the journey from Egypt, after years of slavery, to freedom in the Holy Land (the story of Moses). Families and friends gather for a traditional dinner, or Seder, typically on the first night, to re-tell the Exodus story and remember the significance of the holiday. During the eight days, those who observe Passover avoid all leavened grain products (wheat, rye, barley, oats, and spelt) and eat matzo (unleavened bread) instead. This is because the Jews left Egypt in such a hurry that they were told to make their bread without yeast as it would not have time to rise. During the Seder meal, the Haggadah is read and the Seder plate is prepared, which together tell the story of the Jewish Exodus from Egypt and explains the traditions and symbols used during the holiday.

ENGAGED LISTENING

If you have access to the Internet, search for video clips that include lyrics for each of the songs mentioned above so you and your loved one can sing and follow along. Ask your loved one if there are any special passages that he or she recites while observing Passover.

MEANINGFUL DISCUSSION

* Passover tells the story of Moses leading the Israelites out of Egypt. What made Moses a great leader? What characteristics are important to you when you look for a leader or when you want to lead by example?

* During the Seder, who is asked to say the four questions also known as Mah Nishtanah? (The youngest person in attendance)

* Did you ever host a Seder? If so, did you have any special traditions?

* During the start of the Seder, a piece of matzo is broken and set aside. During your traditional meal was the matzo ever hidden to be found later on? If so, did the parents or the children go and find it? Was there a special gift for the one who found it?

* What else can you tell me about celebrating Passover? Why is this holiday meaningful to you?

EASTER

SONGS TO USE

CHRIST THE LORD IS RISEN TODAY *1739 Charles Wesley (writer), Various Artists*
EASTER PARADE *1933 Irving Berlin (writer), Judy Garland & Fred Astaire (recommended artist)*
HERE COMES PETER COTTONTAIL *1950 Steve Nelson & Jack Rollins (writers),*
Gene Autry (recommended artist)

ADDITIONAL INFORMATION ABOUT THE HOLIDAY

Christianity's most important holiday, Easter celebrates the resurrection of Christ Jesus. Outside Orthodox churches, Easter does not occur on the same date each year, but rather occurs on the first Sunday following the full moon after the vernal (spring) equinox and can occur anytime between March 22nd and April 25th. In a secular sense, Easter is often a celebration of springtime and is associated with the Easter bunny, colorful eggs, new outfits, and baskets of treats.

ENGAGED LISTENING

While listening with your loved one, sway side to side along with the songs "Easter Parade" and "Here Comes Peter Cottontail." Tap your toes along with the beat and encourage your loved one to do the same. If your loved one follows the Christian faith, encourage him or her to sing the "Alleluia"s that occur frequently throughout the song "Christ the Lord is Risen Today."

MEANINGFUL DISCUSSION

* What do you think of when you think of Easter?
* What are some ways people celebrate Easter? What is one of your favorite ways to celebrate Easter?
* Did you ever participate in an Easter egg hunt? Are you good at finding the eggs?
* Have you decorated Easter eggs before? How did you decorate them?
* Does your family have any special Easter traditions? What about favorite Easter foods or recipes?

If your loved one is struggling with responses to the above questions, use some of the following ideas as prompts: going to church, buying/wearing a new outfit or Easter hat, decorating with flowers, Easter lilies, seeing family, Easter dinner, Easter baskets, candy, chocolate rabbits, Easter egg hunt, decorating eggs, Easter bunny, etc.

CINCO DE MAYO

SONGS TO USE

BESAME MUCHO *1940 Consuelo Velázquez, Javier Solis, Andrea Bocelli (recommended artists)*
CIELITO LINDO *1882 Quirino Mendoza y Cortés (writer), Pedro Infante, Trini Lopez (recommended artists)*
DE COLORES *Traditional, Jose-Luis Orozco, Joan Baez (recommended artists)*
LA BAMBA *1958 Traditional, Ritchie Valens (recommended artist)*
TEQUILA *1958 Daniel Flores (writer), The Champs (recommended artist)*

ADDITIONAL INFORMATION ABOUT THE HOLIDAY

Cinco de Mayo, Spanish for "Fifth of May," is a celebration of the Mexican Army's victory over French forces on May 5, 1862, at the Battle of Puebla. It is often mistaken to be a celebration of Mexican Independence Day, which is actually observed on September 16th. Cinco de Mayo has grown to be even more popular in the United States than in Mexico, and is often a celebration of Mexican-American culture.

ENGAGED LISTENING

If you have access to the Internet, search for images of traditional Mexican-American culture including sombreros, maracas, colorful dresses, and the Mexican flag. You can also find pictures of Mexico including beaches, famous landmarks, cities, outdoor markets, etc. Encourage your loved one to dance along with you as you listen to "De Colores." Hold his or her hands and sway from side to side, raising hands up and down during the chorus of the song. As you listen to "La Bamba," encourage your loved one to shake his or her shoulders and hips from side to side with the beat of the music.

MEANINGFUL DISCUSSION

* What do you think of when you think of Cinco de Mayo? What are some ways people celebrate Cinco de Mayo? (Prompt with examples as needed, such as dancing, listening to mariachi or Latin music, drinking margaritas, parades, dressing up or wearing the colors of the Mexican Flag (green, white and red), displaying the Mexican Flag, hanging a piñata for the children, enjoying traditional Mexican dishes, having a "fiesta," etc.)

* Do you enjoy Mexican food? What are some of your favorite dishes? (Prompt with examples as needed, such as enchiladas, tacos, burritos, migas, tamales, mole, homemade corn chips and tortillas, chile rellenos, flautas, quesadillas, guacamole, flan, etc.)

* Have you ever been to Mexico? What do you remember about it? (Use the pictures from above and/or any personal items your loved one has shared to prompt discussion.)

* The song "Cielito Lindo" is about a beautiful woman and the chorus describes how singing gladdens the heart. Does singing help you feel better? What is your favorite song to listen to when you are feeling down?

MEMORIAL DAY AND VETERANS DAY

SONGS TO USE

ANCHORS AWEIGH *official song of the U.S. Navy*
THE ARMY GOES ROLLING ALONG/THE CAISSON SONG *official song of the U.S. Army*
THE MARINES' HYMN *official song of the U.S. Marine Corps*
SEMPER PARATUS *official song of the U.S. Coast Guard*
THE U.S. AIR FORCE (OFF WE GO . . .) *official song of the U.S. Air Force*
THE BATTLE HYMN OF THE REPUBLIC *Traditional/Various Artists*
THE STARS AND STRIPES FOREVER *1896 John Philip Sousa (writer)*
THE WASHINGTON POST MARCH *1889 John Philip Sousa (writer)*

ADDITIONAL INFORMATION ABOUT THE HOLIDAY

Though they are commonly confused with one another, Memorial Day and Veterans Day celebrate two different things. Memorial Day, observed on the last Monday in May, is a day to commemorate the lives of those who died while serving in the country's armed forces. Veterans Day, observed on November 11th, is a day to honor all United States military veterans. Both days are federal holidays in the United States, and are often celebrated with flags, patriotic music, and parades.

ENGAGED LISTENING

Encourage your loved one to march along to the "Stars and Stripes Forever" and "The Washington Post March." If you have access to the Internet, search for pictures of uniformed military personnel in each of the different branches of the armed forces, logos/symbols/insignias of each branch of the military, and monuments that honor those who have served in each branch of the military to aid the meaningful discussion below.

MEANINGFUL DISCUSSION

* Have you, your spouse, other members of your family, or your friends ever served in the military? If so, what branch(es)? When and how long did you (they) serve? What was your (their) job? Where were you (they) stationed? What was your (their) rank?

* If you did serve in the military, how do you feel about your time with the armed services? What do you remember the most about being in the military? What did you like the most about being in the military? What was the hardest part about being in the military?

* Can you name the five branches of the United States military? (Army, Navy, Air Force, Marines, Coast Guard) Do or did you know anyone who has served/is currently serving in any of those branches? Who?

* If you did not serve in the military, did you help on the home front during the war? If so, how?

INDEPENDENCE DAY

SONGS TO USE

AMERICA THE BEAUTIFUL *1910 Samuel A. Ward (music), Katharine Lee Bates (lyrics)*
GOD BLESS AMERICA *1938 Irving Berlin (writer)*
THE STAR-SPANGLED BANNER *1889 John Stafford Smith (music), Francis Scott Key (lyrics)*
YANKEE DOODLE *Traditional/Various Artists*
YANKEE DOODLE BOY *1904 George M. Cohan (writer)*
YOU'RE A GRAND OLD FLAG *1906 George M. Cohan (writer)*

ADDITIONAL INFORMATION ABOUT THE HOLIDAY

Independence Day, also referred to as the Fourth of July, celebrates the anniversary of the adoption of the Declaration of Independence on July 4, 1776, by the Continental Congress. This marked the formation of the United States of America as an independent nation, separate from the British Empire.

ENGAGED LISTENING

Many well-known patriotic songs are appropriate for the celebration of this holiday. Encourage your loved one to sing along to any of the songs listed above. During the "Star-Spangled Banner," encourage your loved one to place a hand over his or her heart (or, if able, stand at attention if he or she is current or former military).

MEANINGFUL DISCUSSION

* What do we celebrate on Independence Day? (The signing of the Declaration of Independence, and the birthday of the United States.)

* What are some ways you have celebrated the 4th of July? (Prompt with examples as needed, such as barbecues, picnics, fireworks, swimming, parades, family reunions, concerts in the park, wearing red, white, and blue, etc.)

* Many towns and cities will host a parade on the 4th of July. Have you ever attended or participated in local parades? If so, how?

* What are the colors of the American flag? (red, white, and blue) How many stars are on the flag? (50) What do they stand for? (The fifty states in the United States) How many stripes? (13) What do they stand for? (The original thirteen colonies) Were there always 50 stars and 13 stripes? (No, originally there were 13 stars and 13 stripes, and then 15 stars and 15 stripes. In 1818, the stripes were fixed at 13 and at that time it was agreed to add a star for each new state admitted to the union.)

* Are you proud to be an American? If so, what makes you proud to be a part of this country?

HALLOWEEN

SONGS TO USE

THE MONSTER MASH *1962 Bobby Pickett & Lenny Capizzi (writers), Bobby Pickett (artist)*
PURPLE PEOPLE EATER *1958 Sheb Wooley (writer/artist)*
THE WITCH DOCTOR *1958 David Seville (writer/artist)*
WITCHCRAFT *1957 Cy Colman (music), Carolyn Lee (lyrics), Frank Sinatra (artist)*

ADDITIONAL INFORMATION ABOUT THE HOLIDAY

Halloween is thought to have evolved from an ancient Celtic festival called Samhein. Today, Halloween is a light-hearted holiday that is observed primarily by children going door to door in costume asking for candy. While trick or treating did not start in the United States until World War II, the tradition of pranks or tricks on Halloween dates back to the late 1800s. The celebration of Halloween often includes carved pumpkins (jack-o-lanterns), orange and black decorations, and "scary" decorations such as tombstones, witches, spider webs, bats, and monsters.

ENGAGED LISTENING

Encourage your loved one to dance along as you listen to "The Monster Mash." Hold his or her hands to dance together, or provide a variety of simple movement for him or her to imitate, such as tapping toes, shaking shoulders, swaying side to side, and doing "the twist." If you have access to the Internet, search for images of children in costume on Halloween, jack-o-lanterns, skeletons, witches, bats, monsters, ghosts, and Halloween decorations to view with your loved one to aid in the discussion below.

MEANINGFUL DISCUSSION

* What do you think of when you think of Halloween? What are some ways people celebrate Halloween? What are some ways people decorate for Halloween? (Prompt with examples as needed, such as trick or treating, costumes, costume parties, candy, bobbing for apples, pumpkins, jack-o-lanterns, spider webs, bats, ghosts, skeletons, monsters, witches, the colors orange and black, playing pranks or tricks on others, etc.)

* Did you ever play a prank on someone for Halloween? What pranks did you pull?

* Did you ever dress up and go trick or treating? Did you prefer to dress up as something scary, funny, or handsome/beautiful? Do you remember what any of your costumes were? (Prompt with examples as needed, such as witch, ghost, skeleton, monster, mummy, princess, ballerina, fairy, pirate, cowboy, doctor, etc.) Did you ever make your own costume or a costume for a family member or friend?

* What are some of your favorite candies to eat or hand out on Halloween? (Prompt with examples as needed, such as Milky Way, Snickers, Reese's Cups, M&M's, Hershey Kisses, jawbreakers, Kit Kats, licorice, gum, etc.)

THANKSGIVING

SONGS TO USE

COUNT YOUR BLESSINGS *(hymn) Traditional/Various Artists*
OVER THE RIVER AND THROUGH THE WOOD *1844 Lydia Maria Child (writer), Various Artists*
WE GATHER TOGETHER *1597/1626 Traditional/Various Artists*

ADDITIONAL INFORMATION ABOUT THE HOLIDAY

The Pilgrims set sail from England on the Mayflower, in search of religious freedom. They arrived on Plymouth Rock in Massachusetts on December 11, 1620. Their first winter in America was extremely difficult due to the cold weather and lack of food. That following spring, the Native Americans taught the Pilgrims how to effectively grow and harvest crops. The harvest of 1621 was bountiful, and the Pilgrims invited the Native Americans to share in their feast. This became known as the first Thanksgiving. Over the years, the colonies and states continued to celebrate the holiday, however, it was not proclaimed a national holiday until President Abraham Lincoln recognized it as such. In 1941, Congress sanctioned Thanksgiving as a legal, national holiday, occurring annually on the fourth Thursday in November.

ENGAGED LISTENING

While listening to "Over the River and Through the Wood," encourage your loved one to sing along and tap his or her toes throughout. Encourage your loved one to sing "Count Your Blessings" along with you.

MEANINGFUL DISCUSSION

- Do you have any Thanksgiving traditions? (Prompt with examples as needed, such as sharing a meal with family and friends, watching or playing football, sharing what you are thankful for, watching the Macy's Thanksgiving Day Parade, donating food to a local food bank, etc.)

- What are some of your favorite foods to have on the Thanksgiving table? (Prompt with examples as needed, such as turkey, stuffing/dressing, gravy, mashed potatoes, green bean casserole, cranberry sauce, sweet potatoes, sweet potato pie, pumpkin pie, pecan pie, etc.)

- The week of Thanksgiving is one of the busiest times to travel during the year. Do (did) you ever travel for this holiday? If so, where did you go and who did you visit?

- What are you looking forward to the most when celebrating Thanksgiving?

- What are some things you are thankful for?

CHRISTMAS

SONGS TO USE

There is a myriad of beloved Christmas songs you can enjoy with your loved one.
*Please refer to the Christmas playlist in **Part Two**, on page 34, for some top favorites.*

ADDITIONAL INFORMATION ABOUT THE HOLIDAY

Christmas is the Christian celebration of the birth of Jesus. In a secular sense, the holiday includes festive decorations and the arrival of the mythical Santa Claus, who visits and rewards good children with presents under the tree and in their stockings.

ENGAGED LISTENING

If your loved one is able, have him or her choose some favorite songs from the Christmas playlist. Otherwise, read aloud three choices and have him or her pick. While listening, encourage your loved one to sing along with you.

MEANINGFUL DISCUSSION

* What do you think of when you think of Christmas?
* What are some ways to celebrate Christmas? What are some of your favorite ways to celebrate Christmas?
* What are some ways you decorate your home for the holiday season?
* Does your family have any special Christmas traditions? What about favorite Christmas foods or recipes?
* When you were younger, did you believe in Santa? Did you ever get a gift for Christmas that was extra special? What was it? Why was it special to you?
* If you attend church on Christmas Eve, what is the service like? What does the church look like?
* Have you ever experienced a white Christmas? If so, where? Do you enjoy the snow?
* What are you looking forward to the most this Christmastime?

IDEAS TO INCLUDE IN THE ABOVE DISCUSSION

Christmas celebrations may include: decorating the Christmas tree; hanging lights on the outside of the house; hanging up stockings; buying, wrapping, and exchanging gifts; baking and decorating Christmas cookies; listening to Christmas music or going Christmas caroling; getting together with friends and family; enjoying a big Christmas dinner; attending holiday parties; going to church on Christmas Eve or Christmas Day; sending and receiving Christmas cards; going out to look at Christmas lights; etc.

Favorite Christmas foods may include: turkey and dressing, ham, sweet potatoes, pie, Christmas cookies, candy canes, gingerbread, fruitcake, fudge, hot chocolate, egg nog, etc.

About the Authors

Meredith Faith Hamons, MT-BC

Meredith Faith Hamons is a board-certified music therapist and the founder of North Austin Music Therapy. Her company focuses on providing services to older adults in all levels of care, those with neurological impairments, and clients with developmental disabilities. Meredith received her degree in music therapy from Duquesne University in Pittsburgh, Pennsylvania and completed her internship at the San Antonio State Hospital in San Antonio, Texas. She received additional training in Neurologic Music Therapy from the Center for Biomedical Research in Music at Colorado State University. Meredith has been passionate about working with the elderly since she was in high school and was thrilled to create and develop a program for older adults as the foundation of her company. In addition to her clinical work, Meredith also speaks and teaches frequently on the subject of music therapy at state and national conferences. Her first book, *Musically Engaged Seniors*, was published in 2013. Meredith lives in Texas with her amazing husband and wonderful children. When she is not practicing music therapy, her favorite place to be is at the beach with her family.

Tara Parks Jenkins, MT-BC

Tara Parks Jenkins is a board-certified music therapist. She received her bachelor's degree in music therapy from Shenandoah University in 2007. Tara specializes in working with older adults in independent and assisted living, memory care, adult day programs, and home visits. She has extensive training and knowledge in caring for those who have dementia, has supervised both observation and practicum students, has presented on music therapy and dementia, and has worked closely with caregivers on how to share music and create meaningful experiences with their loved ones. Tara is passionate about music therapy, is committed to fostering meaningful relationships, and above all loves to engage in shared music experiences with older adults. Tara recently moved to Austin, Texas, and when not practicing music therapy, she enjoys exploring her new city with her husband and their dog.

Cathy Befi-Hensel, MM, MT-BC

Cathy Befi-Hensel has been practicing as a board-certified music therapist since 2010. She received her bachelor's degree in music therapy from the University of the Incarnate Word, and went on to receive her Master of Music degree in music therapy from Sam Houston State University in 2013. She published her first article in the Journal of Music Therapy in 2014, and received additional training in Neurologic Music Therapy in 2015. Cathy is currently an adjunct professor at the University of the Incarnate Word, where she teaches undergraduate courses in music therapy. Cathy has always had a passion for working with older adults. While she has worked with many different populations as a music therapist, a main focus of her current clinical work is with older adults living in both memory care and assisted living facilities. Cathy lives in Texas, where she loves playing board games with her husband, and spending time with their son and two cats.

References Used in This Book

Appleby, A. (Ed.). (1991). *America's All Time Favorite Songs*. New York/London/Sydney: Amsco Publications.

Cevasco, A. M., & Vanweelden, K. (2010). An analysis of songbook series for older adult populations. *Music Therapy Perspectives*, 28(1), 37-78.

Cevasco-Trotter, A. M., Vanweelden, K., & Bula, J. A. (2014). Music Therapists' Perception of Top Ten Popular Songs by Decade (1900s-1960s) for Three Subpopulations of Older Adults. *Music Therapy Perspectives*, 32(2), 165-176.

Clair, A. A. (1996). *Therapeutic uses of music with older adults*. Baltimore, MD: Health Professions Press.

Cohen, N. (2014). Music therapy and sociological theories of aging. *Music Therapy Perspectives*, 32(1), 84-92.

Get America Singing Again: A Project of the Music Educators National Conference. (1996). Milwaukee, WI: Hal Leonard.

Hamons, M. (2013). *Musically Engaged Seniors: 40 Session Plans and Resources for a Vibrant Music Therapy Program*. Round Rock, TX: Whelk & Waters Publishing.

Hodges, D. A. (Ed.). (1996). *Handbook of Music Psychology (2nd ed.)*. San Antonio, TX: IMR Press.

Peters, J. (2000) *Music Therapy: An Introduction (2nd ed.)*. Springfield, IL: Charles C. Thomas Publisher.

This is the Real Little Ultimate Fake Book with over 1200 Songs (3rd ed.). (2001). Milwaukee, WI: Hal Leonard.

Taylor, D. (1997). *Biomedical Foundations of Music as Therapy*. Eau Claire, WI: ECPrinting.

Thaut, M. (2008) Rhythm, Music, and the Brain: Scientific Foundations and Clinical Applications. New York and London: Routledge.

Thompson, W. F. (2009). *Music, Thought, and Feeling: Understanding the Psychology of Music*. New York, NY: Oxford University Press.

VanWeelden, K., & Cevasco, A. M. (2007). Repertoire recommendations by music therapists for geriatric clients during singing activities. *Music Therapy Perspectives*, 25(1), 4-12.

Yinger, O. S., & Springer, D. G. (2015). Analyzing Recommended Songs for Older Adult Populations through Linguistic and Musical Inquiry. *Music Therapy Perspectives*, 34(1), 116-125.

Websites

http://www.45cat.com

http://kids.niehs.nih.gov/games/songs/patriotic

http://m.alz.org/facts-and-figures.asp

http://www.aarp.org/home-family/caregiving

http://www.acousticmusicarchive.com

http://www.allmusic.com

http://www.alz.org

http://www.amazon.com

http://www.apple.com/itunes

http://www.balladofamerica.com

http://www.beatlesbible.com

http://www.beatlesbyday.com

http://www.billboard.com

http://www.biography.com

http://www.breadsite.org

http://www.broadwaymusicalhome.com

http://www.cajunradio.org

http://www.carols.org

http://www.cbmt.org

http://www.civilwarheritagetrails.org

http://www.contemplator.com

http://www.cyberhymnal.org

http://www.dementiatoday.com/brain-plasticity-and-alzheimers-disease

http://www.dorisday.net

http://www.edsullivan.com

http://www.eldersong.com

http://www.entertainment.time.com

http://www.esoterx.com

http://www.folkalley.com

http://www.history.com

http://www.hymnary.org

http://www.hymntime.com

http://www.ibiblio.org

http://www.imdb.com

http://www.irishmusicdaily.com

http://www.jazzstandards.com

http://www.jewfaq.org/holidaya.htm

http://www.johnnycash.com

http://www.knowla.org

http://www.loc.gov

http://www.lutheran-hymnal.com

http://www.lyricsplayground.com

http://www.mayoclinic.org/diseases-conditions/dementia/home/ovc-20198502

http://www.mentalfloss.com

http://www.music.army.mil

http://www.musichealth.net

http://www.musicnotes.com

http://www.musictherapy.org

http://www.negrospirituals.com

http://www.newsyearsfavors.com

http://www.npr.org

http://www.oscars.org

http://www.parlorsongs.com

http://www.performingsongwriter.com/god-bless-america

http://www.rollingstone.com

http://www.salon.com

http://www.scotland.org

http://www.secondhandsongs.com

http://www.sftradjazz.org

http://www.songfacts.com

http://www.songsforteaching.com

http://www.spotify.com

http://www.stageagent.com

http://www.tasteofcountry.com

http://www.teepasnow.com

http://www.theatrehistory.com

http://www.thoughtco.com/folk-4132893

http://www.time.com

http://www.timeanddate.com

http://www.timeout.com

http://www.va.gov

http://www.wikipedia.org

http://www.youtube.com

Made in the USA
San Bernardino, CA
26 August 2017